My First Catechism Activity Book

Answer Key

CONCORDIA PUBLISHING HOUSE · SAINT LOUIS

Contents

The Ten Commandments

(MFC 7)

Words to Use

Moses
Sinai
Egypt
mountain
two
Ten Commandments
slavery

1. God's people once lived in the land of **Egypt**.

2. God's people once lived under the control of others in **slavery**.

3. After God rescued His people, He brought them to a **mountain**.

4. **Sinai** was the name of the place where God talked to Moses.

5. God gave the commandments to **Moses** and to God's people.

6. God wrote the commandments on **two** pieces of stone.

7. In all God wrote Ten Commandments.

According to God's Word

1. God gave us the Ten Commandments because He (**loves**—fears) us.

2. The commandments tell us how to (covet—**live**).

3. God sent (Moses—**Jesus**) to earn forgiveness for the times we break the commandments.

In Words of My Own

1. Describe God coming down to the mountain to give Moses and the people the Ten Commandments. **God came down with lightning and thunder and smoke and fire.**

2. What is God like? **God loves us. We know He loves us because He sent Jesus to be our Savior.**

3. Why did God give us the Ten Commandments? **God gave us the Ten Commandments because He loves us and wants us to know what kinds of thoughts and actions are pleasing to Him.**

4

The First Commandment
(MFC 8)

Words to Use

angel
king
statue
worship
furnace

1. A wicked **king** once ordered the people to worship an idol he had made.

2. The idol was in the form of a **statue**.

3. Three men who believed in God refused to **worship** any god but the true God.

4. The three who believed in God were thrown into a **furnace**.

5. God sent His **angel** to save the three men.

According to God's Word

1. Three (**men**—statues) trusted in the true God.

2. (**God**—the king) saved the three men.

3. "Come out of the furnace!" called the king. "There is no god like your God. He (trusts—**saves**) His people!"

In Words of My Own

1. What does it mean to worship? **To worship is to praise, honor, and serve something.**

2. What things do you sometimes allow to take God's place? **Answers will vary.**

3. When has God saved you? **Jesus paid for my sins when He suffered and died on the cross. Other examples of God's intervention on behalf of individual students will vary.**

The First Commandment

(MFC 9)

Words to Use

Isaac

ram

altar

Jesus

Abraham

1. **Abraham** had a son named Isaac.

2. Both **Isaac** and his father were willing to obey God.

3. God tested Abraham's faith by asking him to sacrifice his son on an **altar**.

4. God provided a **ram** for the sacrifice.

5. **Jesus** willingly sacrificed Himself to save us.

According to God's Word

1. Once God told a father and son to travel to a (river—**mountaintop**).

2. Here a (**sacrifice**—bargain) was to be made.

3. God (**tested**—took) Abraham's faith.

4. (**God**—Jesus) is the father who sacrificed His Son to pay for the sins of the world.

In Words of My Own

1. What does it mean to sacrifice? **To sacrifice means to give something precious to a deity.**

2. Explain the relationship between having faith and obeying. **God's people put their faith into action in lives of obedience when, through the working of the Holy Spirit, they obey God's Word.**

3. What does Jesus' sacrifice mean to you? **Answers will vary.**

The Second Commandment
(MFC 10)

Words to Use

slingshot

Goliath

David

giant

shepherd

1. A **giant** once came out onto a battlefield where he spoke against God and His people.

2. When David came out onto the battlefield, **Goliath** cursed him.

3. David was a **shepherd** boy.

4. David killed the giant using a **slingshot**.

5. **David** trusted in God.

According to God's Word

1. The giant wanted someone to (trust—**fight**) him.

2. The giant (**cursed**—defeated) David.

3. David told the giant, "I come against you in the (sight—**name**) of the Lord Almighty.

4. When the (slingshot—**stone**) hit the giant in the forehead, he fell dead.

In Words of My Own

1. What does it mean to do something in the name of the Lord? **To do something in the name of the Lord means to perform an action believing in God and trusting in His promises.**

2. In what way does David battling Goliath remind you of Jesus facing the devil in order to save us? **Just as David battled against the evil Goliath on behalf of the nation of Israel, Jesus took on the devil himself on behalf of all people in order to win our salvation for us.**

3. What does it mean to trust in the Lord? **To trust in the Lord means to rely on Him to provide and care for you.**

The Second Commandment

Words to Use

men

lions

angel

Daniel

king

1. **Daniel** loved God.

2. Evil **men** tricked the king.

3. The lions never touched Daniel because of the **angel** God had sent to protect him.

4. The king knew that God had saved Daniel from the **lions**.

5. The happy **king** proclaimed, "The God of Daniel is the living God."

According to God's Word

1. Daniel prayed to God (**three**—ten) times a day.

2. The king passed a (sign—**law**) saying that no one should pray to God.

3. Daniel never stopped (**praying**—explaining) to God.

4. The king said, "The God of Daniel is the (arresting—**living**) God.

In Words of My Own

1. How has God saved you? **God sent Jesus to live and die in order to save me**.

2. If you were Daniel, what prayer would you offer after being taken out of the lions' den? **I would thank God for saving me**.

The Third Commandment

(MFC 12)

Words to Use

twelve

three

temple

Passover

Jerusalem

1. Jesus was **twelve** years old when he went with Mary and Joseph to Jerusalem.

2. The **Passover** celebration was held in Jerusalem.

3. When Mary and Joseph couldn't find Jesus, they went once again to **Jerusalem**.

4. They searched for Jesus for **three** days.

5. Finally they found Jesus with the teachers in the **temple**.

According to God's Word

1. Clearly, Jesus loved being in (danger—**the temple**).

2. Jesus spoke of being in His (**Father's**—Mother's) house.

3. Jesus was found listening to the (entertainers—**teachers**) and asking them questions.

In Words of My Own

1. What was Jesus' attitude about spending time at the temple? How do you know? **Jesus loved spending time in God's house learning and talking about the things of God. Jesus stayed behind in Jerusalem to spend more time in the temple studying God's Word with the teachers.**

2. In what way is Jesus' Father the same as your father? **Like Jesus, we call God our Father in heaven. Like our fathers on earth, Jesus' Father cares for Him and loves Him.**

3. What do you and others see and do when you are in God's house? **In God's house we hear and learn God's Word; we worship God with hymns, songs, and our offerings; and we pray. Some members receive forgiveness by participating in the Lord's Supper.**

The Third Commandment

(MFC 13)

Words to Use

worried

chosen

working

listening

important

1. Martha was busy **working** to make Jesus' visit pleasant and enjoyable.

2. Mary was **listening** to Jesus' words.

3. Jesus said that Martha was **worried** about many things.

4. Jesus told Martha that one thing is **important**.

5. Mary had **chosen** to hear Jesus' words.

According to God's Word

1. Mary and Martha were (**sisters**—friends).

2. Martha wanted (Jesus—**Mary**) to come and help her.

3. Jesus said that (referring—**listening**) to God's Word is the one important thing.

In Words of My Own

1. Was Martha wrong to serve Jesus as she did? Why or why not? **Answers may vary. Jesus said that Mary had chosen the activity that was most important.**

2. Why is Mary's choice the right choice? **God strengthens and encourages us through His Word.**

3. When do you listen to God's Word? **Answers will vary somewhat but are likely to include when attending church, when participating in a Christian education class, or when taking part in family devotions.**

The Fourth Commandment

(MFC 14)

Words to Use

save

holy

disobey

obey

help

1. Jesus is **holy**.

2. He came to earth to **save** all people.

3. As the Son of God, He was able to **obey** His parents in all things.

4. As Jesus grew, He became more and more of a **help** to His parents.

5. Because of Jesus, we are forgiven for the times we **disobey** our parents.

According to God's Word

1. The Fourth Commandment tells us to (**honor**—worship) our parents.

2. Jesus was once (an angel—**a baby**).

3. Jesus lived a perfect (**life**—lie) in our place.

4. Jesus obeyed His (**Father**—Mother) in heaven.

5. Jesus never (**lied**—spoke) to Mary and Joseph.

In Words of My Own

1. What does it mean to honor one's parents? **To honor one's parents is to respect, obey, and seek to please them.**

2. What did Jesus do for us in our place because we are unable to do it? **Jesus honored Mary and Joseph, as well as His Father in heaven, by a life of complete and willing obedience.**

The Fourth Commandment
(MFC 15)

Words to Use

army
head
justice
handsome
forgiveness

1. Absalom was a **handsome** man.

2. Absalom told the people that if he were king, the people would get **justice**.

3. King David wanted to show love and **forgiveness** to Absalom.

4. Absalom led an **army** against his father David.

5. Absalom died after his **head** became caught in a tree.

According to God's Word

1. Absalom suggested to the people that he would make a good (**king**—soldier).

2 Absalom rode a (**mule**—camel) to escape from David's soldiers.

3 The (rear guard—**commander**) of David's army killed Absalom.

4. At the death of Absalom, David felt (relieved—**sad).**

In Words of My Own

1. How did Absalom sin against the Fourth Commandment? **Absalom rebelled against his father by trying to steal the kingdom from him.**

2. How did David show himself to be a parent who loves the Lord? **David loved Absalom and forgave him.**

3. Why do God's people show love and forgiveness to others? **As the Holy Spirit works through God's Word, He moves followers of Jesus to love and forgive others.**

The Fifth Commandment

(MFC 16)

Words to Use

farmer

shepherd

offering

best

jealous

1. One of the sons of Adam and Eve, Cain, became a **farmer**.

2. Abel, their other son, became a **shepherd**.

3. Both brought their **offering** to the Lord.

4. Abel gave to God from among the **best** that he had.

5. Cain became **jealous** and killed his brother.

According to God's Word

1. God gave Adam and Eve sons after they left the (town—**garden**) of Eden.

2. (**The sons**—Eve) brought gifts to God.

3. God was (angry—**pleased**) with Abel's offering.

4. Jesus, the Savior of the world, came from (**Seth's**—Cain's) family.

5 To murder someone is to (call—**kill**) that person.

In Words of My Own

1. How does the story of Cain and Abel show that one sin often leads to another? **Cain's jealousy toward his brother led him to commit murder.**

2. How does the way Cain and Abel brought their gifts to God differ from how we give God our offerings? **Cain and Abel gave their offerings to God by burning them on an altar; we give offerings to God by placing them in the offering plate during divine worship services.**

3. Why did Jesus come into the world? **Jesus came into the world to pay the penalty for all sins, including the sin of murder.**

The Fifth Commandment
(MFC 17)

Words to Use

thieves

story

enemy

help

wounds

1. Jesus once told a **story**.

2. Jesus told about a man who was attacked by **thieves**.

3. The person who helped the wounded man was really his **enemy**.

4. The man who came to help bandaged the injured man's **wounds**.

5. Like the man who showed kindness, Jesus came to **help** and save us.

According to God's Word

1. In Jesus' story a man traveled from (**Jerusalem**—Bethlehem) to Jericho.

2. Some thieves robbed and (insulted—**wounded**) the man.

3. The thieves left the man half (awake—**dead**).

4. Samaritans and (Jesus—**Jews**) were enemies.

5. The Good Samaritan reminds us of (the wounded man—**Jesus**).

In Words of My Own

1. According to the Fifth Commandment, how does God want us to treat other people? **God wants us to help and support our neighbor in every way possible.**

2. Of whom does the wounded man remind us? Explain. **The wounded man reminds us of ourselves and all people in need of help and salvation; all people need the salvation that only Jesus provides.**

3. In what ways is Jesus like the Good Samaritan? **Jesus helps and saves us, even when we rebel against God and treat God as our enemy. He paid the cost of our salvation with His own blood.**

The Sixth Commandment

(MFC 18)

Words to Use

forgive

sin

stone

adultery

ground

1. **Adultery** is a sin that misuses God's gift of marriage.

2. The people asked Jesus whether they might **stone** the woman.

3. To make a point, Jesus wrote on the **ground**.

4. Jesus said that the person without **sin** should throw the first stone.

5. Jesus was willing to **forgive** the woman.

According to God's Word

1. (**Teachers**—Students) brought to Jesus a woman who had been unfaithful to her husband.

2. Jesus wrote on the ground using a (stick—**finger**).

3. The people began to leave until only Jesus and the (man—**woman**) remained.

4. Jesus (**forgave**—scolded) the woman.

5. "(Have—**Leave**) your life of sin," Jesus told the woman.

In Words of My Own

1. In Old Testament times, how were people who committed adultery to be punished? **They were to be stoned to death.**

2. How did Jesus treat the woman who had sinned? **Jesus forgave the woman and told her to leave her life of sin.**

3. How does Jesus treat us when we sin? **Jesus forgives us and all people who come to Him with repentant hearts.**

The Sixth Commandment
(MFC 19)

Words to Use

almighty

marriage

wife

change

husband

1. Because Jesus is God, He has the power to **change** things.

2. Once Jesus attended a wedding where He showed His **almighty** power by changing water into wine.

3. God wants husbands and wives to be happy in their **marriage**.

4. Jesus' love for those who believe in Him is like that of a **husband** for his wife.

5. Jesus reminds us of someone willing to give his life for his **wife**.

According to God's Word

1. Once Jesus attended a wedding in (Jerusalem—**Cana**).

2. Jesus' (**mother**—servant) was also at the wedding.

3. At the wedding Jesus showed that He was (thirsty—**God**).

4. Jesus used His power to make (water—**wine**).

In Words of My Own

1. Jesus once provided refreshments for people at a wedding. For which of the things Jesus has provided you are you especially thankful today? **Answers will vary.**

2. At the wedding in Cana, how did Jesus show Himself to be God? **Jesus performed a miracle; He changed water into wine.**

3. God wants husbands and wives to love one another as Jesus loves all people. Describe this kind of love. **Jesus put our need for salvation ahead of His own needs; He willingly gave His life for us. God's love empowers husbands and wives to have this kind of sacrificial love for one another.**

The Seventh Commandment

(MFC 20)

Words to Use

victory
stole
promised
forgive
hidden

1. God brought His people safely into the land He had **promised** them.

2. God brought the people **victory** over Jericho.

3. Achan disobeyed; he **stole** things for himself.

4. Nothing can be **hidden** from God.

5. Jesus died to **forgive** all sins.

According to God's Word

1. God told the people not to (**take**—destroy) anything from the city of Jericho.

2. Achan (obeyed—**disobeyed**) God.

3. Achan (**hid**—sold) the things he had taken from Jericho.

4. Jesus (ignores—**forgives**) all sins, including the sin of stealing.

In Words of My Own

1. What is stealing? **Stealing is taking those things for our own that are not ours.**

2. What kinds of things do people steal from one another? **Answers will vary somewhat. People steal things you can see, such as money or possessions; they also steal things like love, a good name, and happiness from others.**

3. How can we be sure that we can be forgiven for stealing? **Jesus offers forgiveness for all sins. Since He earned forgiveness for all sins through His own life, death, and resurrection, we can be sure of His forgiveness for stealing.**

The Seventh Commandment
(MFC 21)

Words to Use

heart

taxes

possessions

cheated

short

1. Zacchaeus was very rich; he was also **short**.

2. Zacchaeus worked collecting people's **taxes**.

3. Jesus changed the **heart** of Zacchaeus.

4. Zacchaeus promised to give half his **possessions** to the poor.

5. Zacchaeus said that if he had **cheated** anyone, he would repay four times the amount.

According to God's Word

1. Zacchaeus was a (poor—**rich**) collector of taxes.

2. Zacchaeus wanted to see (**Jesus**—a sycamore-fig tree).

3. Jesus (**changed**—scared) Zacchaeus.

In Words of My Own

1. How has Jesus changed you? **He has changed each believer from an enemy of God to a follower of God through faith in Christ Jesus. Answers will vary.**

2. What did Jesus mean when He said, "I have come to seek and save the lost"? **Jesus came to find all who are lost in sin so that He might save them and give them forgiveness and eternal life.**

The Eighth Commandment
(MFC 22)

Words to Use

evidence

false

trial

truth

1. Jesus' enemies brought Him to stand **trial** before the leaders of the day.

2. The court needed **evidence** in order to put Jesus to death.

3. Though many witnesses came before the court, their statements about Jesus were all **false**.

4. When the chief priest asked Jesus whether He was the Christ, the Son of God, Jesus spoke the **truth**.

According to God's Word

1. The false witnesses did not (fight—**agree**) with one another.

2. The chief priest asked Jesus (**directly**—secretly) if He was the Son of God.

3. When Jesus spoke, He always spoke (kindly—**the truth**).

4. Jesus' words made the chief priest (happy—**angry**).

In Words of My Own

1. Why is it strange that Jesus was placed on trial? **Jesus was innocent of any wrong doing.**

2. Why was Jesus willing to suffer persecution, arrest, and trial? **Because of His great love for all people, Jesus willingly suffered in order to earn forgiveness, new life, and eternal salvation for them.**

3. Why is it important to you that Jesus answered the chief priest's question with "Yes"? **Jesus had to be the very Son of God in order to forgive and save us.**

The Eighth Commandment

Words to Use

well

enemy

friend

defend

1. Jonathan was David's **friend**.

2. King Saul treated David as an **enemy**.

3. Jonathan spoke **well** of David.

4. Jonathan spoke to **defend** David before Saul.

According to God's Word

1. King Saul (loved—**hated**) David.

2. Jonathan gave David (**gifts**—trouble).

3. Jonathan spoke (**well**—evil) of David before King Saul.

4. Jonathan's love for David reminds us of the love (David—**Jesus**) has for us.

In Words of My Own

1. By what kinds of words do we break the Eighth Commandment? **We break the Eighth Commandment by speaking words that are untrue or hurtful to others**.

2. What message does Jesus bring to His Father about us and our sins? **Jesus speaks to our Father in heaven on our behalf, telling Him that He has died to take the punishment for our sins.**

3. What gifts has your friend Jesus given to you? **Jesus has earned forgiveness for all our sins, new life, and eternal salvation for us.**

The Ninth Commandment

(MFC 24)

Words to Use

vineyard

crime

sulked

planned

brooded

1. Ahab coveted the **vineyard** of Naboth.

2. Ahab **sulked** and **brooded** when Naboth refused to sell the vineyard to him.

3. Jezebel **planned** an evil scheme to get the vineyard for Ahab.

4. Jezebel told people to lie by saying that Naboth had committed a **crime.**

According to God's Word

1. Those who told lies about Naboth broke the (**Eighth**—Seventh) Commandment.

2. Naboth's death was a sin against the (**Fifth**—Sixth) Commandment.

3. Jesus died to earn (justice—**forgiveness**) for all sins, including the sins of Ahab and Jezebel.

In Words of My Own

1. Sometimes one sin leads a person to commit still others. Explain this truth using the example in the story of Naboth's vineyard. **The sin of coveting led to the sins of lying and murder.**

2. What does it mean to covet? **To covet something is to have a sinful desire to obtain something someone else owns.**

3. How did Jesus earn forgiveness of all sins, including the sin of coveting? **Jesus lived a sinless life and died in our place to earn forgiveness for our sins.**

The Ninth Commandment

Words to Use

nephew

rescue

reward

tenth

possessions

1. Lot was a **nephew** of Abraham.

2. Abraham rescued Lot and his neighbors and their **possessions**.

3. The king wanted to give Abraham a **reward**.

4. Instead of receiving things, Abraham gave things to God; Abraham gave Melchizedek a **tenth** of all he had acquired in battle.

5. Long after the time of Abraham, God sent Jesus to **rescue** us and all people.

According to God's Word

1. Once enemies came to carry away the (**people**—leaders) of Sodom and their possessions.

2. After Abraham rescued the people, the king wanted to give Abraham a (city—**reward**).

3. Abraham (**refused**—accepted) the king's offer.

4. Abraham gave God gifts, presenting them to (**Melchizedek**—Sodom).

5. God sent Jesus to give us salvation—the greatest (**gift**—enemy) of all.

In Words of My Own

1. How do the actions of Abraham differ from those of Ahab and Jezebel? **Rather than wanting things for himself, as Ahab and Jezebel did, Abraham offered his possessions to God.**

2. When and where do you give God your offerings of thanks? **We give God our offerings when we assemble with other Christians to worship and learn about God.**

3. In what ways has Jesus rescued you? **Jesus has rescued us from sin, death, and the power of the devil.**

The Tenth Commandment
(MFC 26)

Words to Use

terrible

repented

husband

coveted

prophet

1. David set into motion a plan to kill Bathsheba's **husband**.

2. The **prophet** Nathan came to call David to account because of his sin.

3. David's sin was **terrible**.

4. David **coveted** the wife of another man.

5. When David **repented**, God forgave him for Jesus' sake.

According to God's Word

1. David looked out from his (**palace**—temple) and saw Bathsheba.

2. David (**coveted**—hated) Bathsheba.

3. David broke the (**Fifth**—Sixth) commandment when he had Bathsheba's husband killed.

4. David broke the (Fifth—**Sixth**) commandment when he interfered with Bathsheba's marriage.

5. In response to Nathan's accusation, David (**repented**—rejoiced).

In Words of My Own

1. In what way did Jesus pay for all the terrible things all people have done? **Jesus lived a sinless life and died on the cross to pay for all sins.**

2. What comfort does Jesus bring to all who repent of their sin? **Jesus forgives us, removing our sins from us.**

The Tenth Commandment
(MFC 27)

Words to Use

submit

disrespect

serve

rest

1. Sarah treated Hagar poorly, and Hagar treated Sarah with **disrespect**.

2. As Hagar was running away, she sat down by a spring to **rest**.

3. At the well, the angel of the Lord came to Hagar and told her to go back and **submit** to Sarah.

4. Just as Jesus loves and serves us, He leads us to love, **serve**, and submit to one another.

According to God's Word

1. Abraham's wife was named (**Sarah**—Hagar).

2. Hagar was running away when she came to a spring in the (forest—**desert**).

3. The angel of the Lord told Hagar to go back to Sarah. "(Abraham—**God**) will bless you," the angel said.

4. (**Hagar**—Sarah) did as the angel had said.

5. God sent Jesus to pay for the (**wrongs**—favors) we have done.

In Words of My Own

1. According to the explanation of the Tenth Commandment, how does God want people to treat one another? **God does not want us to entice or force away from our neighbor his people and animals, but He wants us to urge them to stay and do their duty.**

2. After urging her to return and do her duty, what promise did the angel give to Hagar? **The angel told Hagar that God would bless her.**

3. Why do God's people love, serve, and submit to one another? **Jesus leads us to love, serve, and submit to one another, just as He loved, served, and submitted to His Father.**

The Close of the Commandments

(MFC 28)

Words to Use

walked

wicked

outside

grief

inside

1. The behavior of the people filled God's heart with **grief**.

2. Noah loved God; the Bible says that Noah **walked** with God.

3. God sent a flood; everything **inside** the ark was saved.

4. God destroyed every living thing **outside** the ark.

According to God's Word

1. God told Noah to (buy—**build**) an ark, a large boat.

2. God told Noah to assemble his (**family**—neighbors) and two of every kind of animal inside the ark.

3. God sent a flood to (**destroy**—save) every living thing outside the ark.

In Words of My Own

1. Noah and his family were also sinners. Why didn't God destroy them? **Noah walked with God; this means that Noah and his family believed and trusted in God. The faith God had given them saved them.**

2. In what way does the ark remind you of the church? **God gave His gift of salvation to Noah and his family by means of the ark; today God saves us through the gifts of Word and Sacrament that we receive when we attend church.**

The Close of the Commandments

(MFC 29)

Words to Use

worshiped
landed
blessed
safe
reminded

1. God kept Noah, his family, and all the animals with them **safe** inside the ark.

2. As the floodwaters receded, the ark **landed** on a mountaintop.

3. After Noah and his family left the ark, they **worshiped** God.

4. The rainbow God placed into the sky **reminded** Noah, his family, and their descendants that God would never again destroy the world with a flood.

5. God **blessed** Noah and his descendants.

According to God's Word

1. God punishes sin. He once (**destroyed**— blessed) the world with a flood.

2. God placed a rainbow in the sky as a sign of His (**grace**—threats) and promises.

3. God gave Noah and his descendants a (**new**—perfect) life after the flood.

In Words of My Own

1. To whom does God promise "grace and every blessing"? **God promises grace and every blessing to all who keep His commandments.**

2. What new life do all people receive when they come to faith in Jesus? **By the power of the Holy Spirit at work through God's Word, followers of Jesus live a new life of love and obedience toward God and other people.**

3. In what way have you received a new life through water? **In Baptism the Holy Spirit gives us new life as we become forgiven children of God by faith in Christ Jesus.**

The Apostles' Creed

(MFC 33)

Words to Use

born
Trinity
conceived
worship

1. Jesus was **conceived** by the Holy Spirit.

2. Jesus was **born** to a young woman named Mary.

3. Wise Men followed a star so they might **worship** the Savior.

4. The true God is the **Trinity**.

According to God's Word

1. Jesus was born of the (**Virgin**—widow) Mary.

2. We believe in the holy Trinity, (**three**—many) persons, yet only one God.

3. God gives (sudden—**spiritual**) wisdom to those who trust in Him.

4. God wants all people to be (**saved**—crucified) and to come to a knowledge of the truth.

In Words of My Own

1. How would you describe the true God? **The true God is the triune God—three persons, but one God. That is why Christians call God the Trinity.**

2. Name the three persons in the Trinity. **The three persons in the Trinity are the Father, the Son, and the Holy Spirit.**

3. Explain how your Savior is both God and man. **Jesus was conceived by the Holy Spirit, who is God, and born of the Virgin Mary, who was a human being.**

4. What is God's desire for all people? **God wants all people to be saved and to come to a knowledge of the truth.**

The First Article

(MFC 34-35)

Creation

Words to Use

rested

Eden

created

heaven

1. When God made all things from nothing, He **created** them.

2. After making all things in just six days, God **rested**.

3. God gave Adam and Eve a beautiful garden home called **Eden**.

4. One day all who believe in Jesus will live in a beautiful home called **heaven**.

According to God's Word

1. God made all things including the (**sun**—sin).

2. God made the first people, Adam and (Eden—**Eve**).

3. The home of the first people was a beautiful (house—**garden**).

4 There was no (sun—**sin**) in paradise.

5. Because we know Jesus as our (**Savior**—Creator), one day we will live with Him in a happy home.

In Words of My Own

1. How was life for Adam and Eve in the garden different from life in our world? **Adam and Eve lived in happiness and without sin in the garden. Today we live in a world of sin and its unhappy consequences.**

2. What will heaven be like? **In heaven there is complete happiness and no sin.**

3. What unique qualities and abilities has God the Father given you? **Answers will vary.**

4. Describe the new life God the Father has given you in Jesus. **As the Holy Spirit works in my life through Word and Sacrament, God assures me of forgiveness of all my sin, strengthens me to resist temptations, and impels me to help and serve others.**

The Second Article

(MFC 36-37)

Redemption

Words to Use

crucified

Second

only

right

judge

ascended

born

1. Jesus is the **only** Son of God.

2. The work and person of Jesus are described in the **Second** Article.

3. Jesus came to earth when He was conceived by the Holy Spirit and **born** of the Virgin Mary.

4. Jesus paid for my sins with His life when He was **crucified**.

5. Jesus left the earth when He **ascended** into heaven.

6. Now He sits at the **right** hand of God, the Father.

7. One day Jesus will come to earth again to **judge** the living and the dead.

According to God's Word

1. Jesus was (conceived—**begotten**) of the Father from eternity.

2. Jesus is both true (**God**—devil) and true man, the son of Mary.

3. I believe that by nature I am a(n) (innocent—**lost**) person.

4. Jesus redeemed me with His (gold—**blood**).

In Words of My Own

1. From what three evils has Jesus rescued you? **Jesus has rescued me from sin, death, and from the power of the devil.**

2. What does Jesus empower you to do as you live under Him in His kingdom? **Jesus has empowered those who belong to Him to serve Him in everlasting righteousness, innocence, and blessedness.**

3. What does it mean to you that Jesus has risen from the dead and that He lives and reigns to all eternity? **Answers will vary but are likely to relate to responses of praise and thanksgiving that the One who has defeated death lives and reigns throughout eternity and is our Savior and Friend.**

And in Jesus Christ His only Son, our Lord.

(MFC 38)

Words to Use

Easter
die
holy
punishment

1. Jesus lived a **holy** life in my place.

2. Jesus came to earth to **die** for my sins and the sins of all people.

3. Jesus took our **punishment** upon Himself.

4. Jesus rose from the dead on **Easter**.

According to God's Word

1. Jesus came to earth to live a (**sinless**—sinful) life for us.

2. Jesus showed Himself to be true (God—**man**) when He died on the cross.

3. Jesus is (true God—true man—**both true God and true man**).

In Words of My Own

1. Why did Jesus have to obey God in our place? **We are unable to live a holy life and keep all the commandments.**

2. What punishment did Jesus take in our place? **Jesus died on the cross to pay for our sins; He died the death we deserved.**

3. What does it mean for us that Jesus rose from the dead? **Jesus' resurrection proves that He is true God and that He accomplished our salvation for us. It also tells us that one day we who trust in Jesus also will rise from the dead and live with God in heaven.**

Who was conceived by the Holy Spirit.

(MFC 39)

Words to Use

Son
servant
angel
mother
message

1. The **angel** Gabriel came to Mary.

2. Gabriel brought Mary a **message**.

3. Mary asked how she could be a **mother**.

4. Mary was to give birth to the **Son** of God.

5. Mary called herself the Lord's **servant**.

According to God's Word

1. Gabriel told Mary she was highly (**favored**—worshiped).

2. Mary would be the mother of the Son of God, the promised (angel—**Savior**).

3. Gabriel told Mary that the power of the Most High would (**overshadow**—overcome) her.

In Words of My Own

1. Why is Mary a special person? **Mary is special because she is the mother of God's Son.**

2. What is unusual about Mary becoming a mother? **Mary is the mother of Jesus, but Jesus' Father is God Himself.**

3. To whom had God promised to send a Savior? **God promised His Old Testament people, including Adam and Eve, that one of their descendants would be the Savior. As time went on, God identified Judah's family as the family in which the Savior would be born.**

Born of the Virgin Mary.

(MFC 40)

Words to Use

census

hometown

inn

angels

shepherds

1. People were required to return to their family's **hometown**.

2. Family members traveled to take part in a **census**.

3. The **inn** had no room for more travelers.

4. Outside Bethlehem, **shepherds** watched their flocks.

5. **Angels** were the first to announce the Savior's birth.

According to God's Word

1. (**Caesar**—Marcus) Augustus took a census.

2. Mary traveled to Bethlehem with (David—**Joseph**).

3. Mary laid Jesus in a (**mange**r—basket).

4. The shepherds (**hurried**—worried) as they went to Bethlehem.

5. The shepherds told everyone the (**good**—sad) news.

In Words of My Own

1. What does the news of the angels and shepherds mean to you? **Our Savior has been born!**

2. Why is it important to share the good news of the coming of the Savior? **Jesus came to be the Savior of the world. He is the only Savior people will have.**

Suffered under Pontius Pilate.

(MFC 41)

Words to Use

dressed

mocked

whipped

yelled

slapped

twisted

1. At Pilate's order, the soldiers **whipped** Jesus.

2. They **twisted** together a crown of thorns and placed it on Jesus' head.

3. They **mocked** Jesus, making fun of Him.

4. Then they **dressed** Jesus in a purple robe.

5. They **slapped** Jesus in His face.

6. "Crucify Him!" they **yelled**.

According to God's Word

1. Jesus (**suffered**—mocked) because of our sins.

2. (Julius—**Pontius**) Pilate was the governor before whom Jesus stood trial.

3. The soldiers made fun of Jesus by calling Him the (curse—**king**) of the Jews.

4. Pilate said, "I find no basis for a (**charge against**—release of) Him."

5. Jesus endured pain and suffering because He (envies—**loves**) you and me.

In Words of My Own

1. What did Jesus endure because of our sins? **Jesus suffered horrible pain and death.**

2. Describe Jesus' suffering under Pilate. **Soldiers whipped Jesus, they twisted a crown of thorns and placed it on Jesus' head, and they mocked, humiliated, and slapped Him.**

3. How do we know that Jesus cares about us? **We know Jesus cares about us because He endured horrible pain and suffering on our behalf.**

Was Crucified.

(MFC 42)

Words to Use

outside

committed

bowed

into

next to

forgave

asked

1. After nailing Jesus to the cross, the soldiers placed it **into** the ground.

2. Jesus forgave the criminal being crucified **next to** Him.

3. Jesus **forgave** those who were crucifying Him.

4. Jesus **asked** John to care for His mother.

5. Jesus **committed** His Spirit to God.

6. Jesus finally **bowed** His head and died for the sins of the world.

According to God's Word

1. Jesus carried his own (**cross**—drink) to Golgotha.

2. Jesus spoke of God (**forsaking**—forgiving) Him because of our sins.

3. From the cross Jesus said, "It is (criminal—**finished**)."

In Words of My Own

1. What is truly amazing about Jesus' forgiveness? **Jesus forgave the enemies who were tormenting and executing Him.**

2. How did Jesus show Himself to be God while dying on the cross? **As true God, Jesus forgave sins.**

3. How did Jesus show Himself to be human while dying on the cross? **Jesus was thirsty; He showed concern for His mother and His friend; He bled and died.**

4. For whose sins did Jesus suffer and die? **Jesus suffered and died for the sins of all people, including mine.**

Died and Was Buried.

(MFC 43)

Words to Use

Arimathea
spices
Pilate
crucifixion
tomb

1. Joseph was from **Arimathea**.

2. Joseph and Nicodemus received permission from **Pilate**.

3. Joseph and Nicodemus wrapped Jesus' body together with **spices**.

4. They place Jesus in a **tomb**.

5. Jesus was buried near the site of His **crucifixion**.

According to God's Word

1. (**Friends**—enemies) of Jesus asked for His body.

2. They rolled a (log—**stone**) against the entrance to the grave.

3. After burying Jesus, Joseph and Nicodemus went to their (church—**homes**).

In Words of My Own

1. How do we know that Jesus was truly dead? **Jesus' body was prepared for burial and laid in a tomb.**

2. How do we know that Pilate believed Jesus was really dead? **Pilate gave permission for Jesus to be buried.**

3. Tell what we know from God's Word about Jesus' tomb. **It was a new tomb located near the crucifixion site. A large stone that could be rolled against the entrance was nearby.**

He descended into hell.
The third day He rose again from the dead. (MFC 44)

Words to Use

proclaim

rose

rolled

reserved

filled

1. Hell is **reserved** for the devil and those without faith in Jesus.

2. Jesus went to hell to **proclaim** His victory.

3. Jesus **rose** again from the dead.

4. The angel **rolled** the stone away from the entrance to Jesus' tomb.

5. The women were **filled** with joy at the angel's news.

According to God's Word

1. After His (**death**—resurrection) Jesus went to preach to those in hell.

2. Early on Easter morning there was a violent (**earthquake**—murder).

3. The angel came from (**heaven**—hell) to Jesus' tomb.

4. The women hurried (to—**away from**) the tomb after hearing the angel's news.

In Words of My Own

1. Why were the women happy after hearing the angel's news? **From the angel, they had learned that Jesus had risen from the dead.**

2. Why do you think the women were in a hurry after hearing the angel's news? **The women were anxious to tell others the good news.**

3. What does Jesus' resurrection mean to you? **Jesus' resurrection means that, in Jesus, I too have victory over death.**

He ascended into heaven and sits at the right hand of God, the Father Almighty. (MFC 45)

Words to Use

forty

two

one

left

right

1. After His resurrection Jesus spent **forty** days appearing to many people.

2. Jesus **left** His disciples to go to His Father in heaven.

3. Suddenly **two** angels appeared.

4. **One** day Jesus will return.

5. Now Jesus is in heaven at His Father's **right** hand.

According to God's Word

1. Jesus led His disciples to a place near (Jerusalem—**Bethany**).

2. Here Jesus rose from the (**ground**—dead).

3. A cloud (**covered**—lifted) Jesus.

4. As Jesus ascended He (rebuked—**blessed**) the disciples.

5. The Bible says that Jesus will come again (eventually—**soon**).

In Words of My Own

1. Why did Jesus appear to many after His resurrection? **Jesus appeared to many witnesses to show that He was truly alive and to give them confidence as they talked about His resurrection with others.**

2. For what purpose will Jesus come back? **Jesus will return to take us to live with Himself forever in heaven.**

From thence He will come to judge the living and the dead. (MFC 46)

Words to Use

know
promise
judge
live
go

1. God keeps every **promise**.
2. From God's Word we **know** that Jesus will come again.
3. Jesus will come again to **judge** all people.
4. Those who do not believe will **go** to eternal punishment.
5. Those who believe will **live** with Jesus forever.

According to God's Word

1. All (believers—**people**) will see Jesus and recognize Him as God's Son and the Savior of the world.
2. (Believers—**Unbelievers**) will go to eternal punishment in hell.
3. In hell will be the devil and the evil (believers—**angels**).
4. Jesus promises the (**happiness**—struggles) of heaven to those with faith.

In Words of My Own

1. How does heaven differ from hell? **Heaven is a place of eternal happiness where believers live with God; hell is a place of everlasting torment where believers live away from God's presence.**
2. How do people who will go to heaven differ from those who will go to hell? **Those who trust in Jesus will go to heaven; those without faith will go to hell.**
3. Why do you believe you will one day go to heaven? **God keeps every promise; He promises salvation to all who love and trust in Him. I believe His promises are fulfilled in Jesus.**

The Third Article
(MFC 47)

Sanctification

Words to Use

raise

sanctifies

calls

enlightens

forgives

1. The Holy Spirit **calls** us by the Gospel.

2. The Holy Spirit **enlightens** believers with His gifts.

3. The Holy Spirit **sanctifies** believers and keeps us in the true faith.

4. The Holy Spirit **forgives** all our sins and the sins of all believers.

5. One day the Holy Spirit will **raise** us from the dead.

According to God's Word

1. I (can—**cannot**) believe in Jesus by my own reason or strength.

2. The Holy Spirit calls, (**gathers**—dispels), enlightens, and sanctifies us.

3. The Holy Spirit keep us in the one true (**faith**—translation).

4. He (**daily**—poorly) and richly forgives the sins of all believers.

5. On the Last Day He will (**raise**—condemn) me and all the dead.

In Words of My Own

1. How do you know that the Holy Spirit has been at work in your life? **When we believe in Jesus as our Savior, we know the Holy Spirit has been at work in our life. We cannot by our own reason or strength believe in Jesus Christ, our Lord, or come to Him.**

2. What did the Holy Spirit do for you through the Gospel? **The Holy Spirit has called us into God's family, the church, by the Gospel.**

I believe in the Holy Spirit, the holy Christian church, the communion of saints. (MFC 48)

Words to Use

fire
Baptism
fifty
3,000
wind

1. The Holy Spirit came upon God's people **fifty** days after Easter.

2. At the coming of the Holy Spirit the people heard a sound like a mighty **wind**.

3. Then what appeared to be tongues of **fire** separated and appeared on Jesus' followers.

4. Peter preached about Jesus. He spoke about repentance and **baptism**.

5. About **3,000** people became believers on that day.

According to God's Word

1. The Holy Spirit came upon Jesus' followers at the feast of (**Pentecost**—Purim).

2. God's people began to (**speak**—sing) in languages they had not learned.

3. Peter (**preached**—opposed) a powerful sermon about Jesus.

4. By the power of the Holy Spirit at work through Word and Sacraments the Christian (**church**—town) grew.

5. Believers often came (**together**—away) to learn, pray, support, and encourage one another.

In Words of My Own

1. What work does the Holy Spirit do through Baptism? **Through Baptism the Holy Spirit forgives sins.**

2. What benefits does the Holy Spirit bring through the church? **As the Holy Spirit works through the Word and Sacraments, our faith grows strong and we, the people of God, support and encourage one another.**

The forgiveness of sins.

(MFC 49)

Words to Use

inheritance

son

poor

servants

celebration

1. Jesus once told a story about a son who asked for his **inheritance**.

2. After he had wasted the money, the son became very **poor**.

3. Then the son remembered how well his father's **servants** lived.

4. When the son returned, the father welcomed him with gifts and a lavish **celebration**.

5. The forgiving father in the story reminds us of Jesus; the **son** in the story reminds us of ourselves.

According to God's Word

1. The son wasted his money on (**parties**— charity).

2. The son was so poor that he worked feeding (homeless people—**pigs**).

3. The father welcomed the young man as a (**son**—servant).

4. Jesus welcomes us with abundant (**grace**— things) when we come to Him asking for forgiveness.

In Words of My Own

1. What words from the story tell you that the young man was sorry for what he had done, rather than simply sorry he had run out of money? **The son decided to return home to ask his father to let him be a servant.**

2. How did the father show the great love he had for his son? **The father welcomed the son, not as a servant, but as a son.**

3. In what ways does Jesus show His great love for you? **Jesus welcomes and forgives all who come to Him seeking forgiveness and a new beginning. Student answers will vary.**

The resurrection of the body, and the life everlasting. Amen. (MFC 50)

Words to Use

change
heaven
death
life
eyes

1. One day the Holy Spirit will bring to **life** all who have ever lived.

2. Our **eyes** will look on Jesus.

3. Jesus will **change** those who believe in Him.

4. Those who believe will go from **death** to new life.

5. We will live with Jesus in the joy and happiness of **heaven**.

According to God's Word

1. On the Last Day (**even**—only) those who have been dead for many years will see Jesus.

2. Those who believe in Jesus will have glorified (**bodies**—deaths).

3. A (**butterfly**—crown) reminds us of the new life we will have after we have been changed.

4. A (butterfly—**crown**) reminds us of the joy and happiness Jesus will give us in heaven.

In Words of My Own

1. Why will you be among those who receive a glorified body? **Jesus will give glorified bodies to those who believe in Him. I believe Jesus is my Savior.**

2. Describe heaven. **Heaven is a place of joy and happiness—the final home of all who believe in Jesus.**

3. Why will you one day be in heaven? **I believe in Jesus, so I know one day I will live with Him in heaven.**

The Lord's Prayer
(MFC 53)

Words to Use

feed

taught

pray

thanks

1. Jesus **taught** by what He said and by what He did.

2. Jesus' disciples once asked Him to teach them to **pray**.

3. Jesus once gave **thanks** before using His divine power.

4. Jesus used His divine power to **feed** thousands.

According to God's Word

1. Jesus taught His (enemies—**disciples**) to pray.

2. Jesus taught them to pray (**the Lord's Prayer**—the Apostles' Creed).

3. Jesus looked up to (**heaven**—the temple) to give thanks.

4. Jesus prayed to His (Mother—**Father**).

5. Jesus' act of providing food for thousands was a (**miracle**—mistake).

6. Jesus (**broke**—gathered) the loaves after He gave thanks.

In Words of My Own

1. For what purpose did Jesus pray before He fed the thousands of people? **Jesus gave thanks to God.**

2. For what purposes do you pray? **Answers will vary somewhat. God's people pray to thank and praise Him and to make requests for ourselves and others.**

3. Why is the prayer the disciples learned called the Lord's Prayer? **Jesus Himself taught the prayer.**

4. What things have you learned about Jesus from what He said and did? **Answers will vary.**

The Introduction

Our Father, who art in heaven.

Words to Use

gifts

earth

penalty

best

heaven

1. We have a Father in **heaven**.

2. God sent His only Son to **earth**.

3. Our heavenly Father wants those things that are **best** for us.

4. Jesus took the **penalty** we deserve.

5. Our heavenly Father gives good **gifts** to us.

According to God's Word

1. We have a heavenly Father who (**loves**—ignores) us.

2. Jesus took the punishment we (**deserved**—received).

3. God's (**Word**—creation) asks, "Which of you, if his son asks for bread, will give him a stone?"

4. Our heavenly Father gives good gifts to those who (**ask**—tell) Him.

In Words of My Own

1. What kind of things does your Father in heaven desire for you? **Our Father in heaven always wants what's best for us.**

2. According to God's Word, what will God do for those who ask? **Our Father in heaven will give good gifts to those who ask Him.**

3. How do you know your Father in heaven loves you? **Answers will vary. We know our Father in heaven loves us because He sent Jesus to pay the penalty we deserve because of our sins.**

The Introduction
(MFC 55)

What does this mean?

Words to Use

confident

compassion

call

come

children

1. God invites us to **call** Him our Father.

2. God invites us to **come** to Him in prayer.

3. God invites us to be **confident** of His care for us.

4. God has **compassion** on His children.

5. God has made us His **children** because of His great love for us.

According to God's Word

1. Jesus (**taught**—warned) His followers about His Father's love for all people.

2. The Lord has compassion on those who (**fear**—scare) Him.

3. "How great is the love the Father has lavished on us, that we should be called children of God," wrote the Apostle (James—**John**).

In Words of My Own

1. Compare the love of our heavenly Father and that of the best of earthly fathers. **Our heavenly Father loves us with the strongest, purest fatherly love, just as good earthly fathers love their families.**

2. In what aspect of our life does God invite His children to be bold? **God invites us to be bold in prayer—"to ask Him as dear children ask their dear father."**

45

The First Petition
(MFC 56)

Hallowed be Thy name.

Words to Use

bright
John
holiness
listen
prophets

1. Jesus took Peter, James, and **John** to a high mountain.

2. The disciples got a glimpse of the **holiness** of God.

3. Jesus' face and clothes became very **bright**.

4. Old Testament **prophets** appeared.

5. Then God Himself spoke, identifying Jesus as His Son and telling the disciples to **listen** to Him.

According to God's Word

1. On the mountain, the Old Testament figures Moses and (Aaron—**Elijah**) appeared with Jesus.

2. These Old Testament figures talked with Jesus about the (**salvation**—trouble) He would bring to the world.

3. Then God Himself spoke from (**heaven**—Jerusalem).

In Words of My Own

1. Describe Jesus' appearance on the mountain. **Descriptions will vary. Jesus' face and clothes became very bright, Moses and Elijah appeared to talk with Jesus about His saving work, and the voice of God spoke from heaven identifying Jesus as His Son.**

2. For what reasons was God pleased with His Son Jesus? **God was pleased with His Son because of His redeeming, sacrificial work for the salvation of the world.**

The First Petition
(MFC 57)

What does this mean?

How is God's name kept holy?

Words to Use

kingdom

purity

protect

worry

lives

profanes

1. God's name is kept holy when His Word is taught in truth and **purity**.

2. God's name is kept holy when God's children lead holy **lives** according to God's Word.

3. Anyone who teaches and lives contrary to God's Word **profanes** the name of God.

4. We ask God to **protect** us from misusing His name.

5. Jesus told His followers not to **worry**.

6. Jesus told His followers to seek God's **kingdom** and His righteousness.

According to God's Word

1. Jesus taught His (angels—**disciples**) many things about God and His love.

2. "Look at the (**birds**—butterflies)," Jesus said.

3. Jesus said that birds know your heavenly Father (loves—**feeds**) them.

4. "Or, why worry about what you are going to (do—**wear**)," Jesus said.

5. "Look at the (**lilies**—violets) of the field. They don't care about clothes," Jesus said.

In Words of My Own

1. According to Jesus' teaching, how do God's children live so as to keep God's name holy? **God's children keep His name holy when we live according to His holy Word.**

2. For what reason are God's children not to worry? **Our heavenly Father knows what we need and promises to provide for us.**

The Second Petition

(MFC 58)

Thy kingdom come.

Words to Use

favoritism

kingdom

Gentiles

associate

1. Long ago, God's people did not **associate** with people who were different from them.

2. God directed Peter to bring the Good News to the **Gentiles**.

3. Peter said, "Now I know that God does not show **favoritism**."

4. Peter helped bring God's **kingdom** to many people.

According to God's Word

1. Long ago, God's people did not interact with those of other (countries—**cultures**).

2. One day a group of men came to invite Peter to go with them to their (**home-town**—commander), Caesarea.

3. Peter went (around—**with**) them.

4. Peter told the Gentiles that Jesus died to take away (Jewish—**their**) sins.

In Words of My Own

1. What do we pray according to the Second Petition? **We pray "Thy kingdom come."**

2. Why does Jesus want His followers to help extend His kingdom? **God wants His followers to help extend His kingdom so that people from throughout the world come to know Jesus as their Savior and receive the forgiveness, new life, and eternal salvation He freely offers.**

The Second Petition
(MFC 59)

What does this mean?

How does God's kingdom come?

Words to Use

holy Word
Holy Spirit
come
itself
godly

1. God's kingdom comes by **itself**.

2. We pray that it will **come** to us also.

3. God's kingdom comes when God gives us the **Holy Spirit**.

4. The Holy Spirit makes it possible for us to believe His **holy Word**.

5. The Holy Spirit helps us to lead a **godly** life.

According to God's Word

1. Paul and his friend (Peter—**Silas**) once crossed the (city—**sea**) to bring the Good News of Jesus to the people living there.

2. Outside Philippi they met a (**business-woman**—housewife) named Lydia.

3. The Lord (**opened**—hardened) Lydia's heart, and she became a believer.

4. Lydia and her (employers—**family**) were baptized.

5. Lydia invited Paul and his friend to stay in her (town—**house**).

In Words of My Own

1. How did God's kingdom come to Lydia?
   The Lord opened Lydia's heart to the words of Paul and Silas, and she became a believer.

2. How did you receive God's kingdom?
   Answers will vary. Most probably became believers through the Word received at Baptism.

The Third Petition
(MFC 60)

Thy will be done on earth as it is in heaven.

Words to Use

prayed

will

cup

angel

night

1. Jesus went to Gethsemane the **night** before His death.

2. Jesus **prayed** to His Father.

3. Jesus asked His Father to take away the **cup** of His suffering.

4. Jesus asked that His Father's **will** be done.

5. God sent an **angel** to give Jesus strength.

According to God's Word

1. Jesus went to the (**Garden**—Rock) of Gethsemane.

2. Here Jesus prayed the same prayer (**three**—twelve) times.

3. In the Third Petition we ask that God's will be done on (heaven—**earth**).

In Words of My Own

1. How did Jesus pray regarding God's will? **Jesus said, "Let not My will, but Your will, be done."**

2. What was the Father's will regarding Jesus' payment for our sins? **God the Father wanted Jesus to suffer and die to pay the penalty we deserved because of our sins.**

The Third Petition

(MFC 61)

What does this mean?

How is God's will done?

Words to Use

hallow

will

come

world

enemy

telling

persecute

1. God's **will** is good and gracious.

2. God's will is done when His people **hallow** His name.

3. God's will is done when those forces are held in check that do not want to let God's kingdom **come**.

4. The devil, the **world**, and our sinful nature have an evil plan and purpose with regard to God's will.

5. At first Paul was an **enemy** of the people of God.

6. But Jesus appeared to Paul and asked Paul, "Why do you **persecute** Me?"

7. God's will for Paul's life was to travel the world, **telling** people about Jesus.

According to God's Word

1. God's will is done when He strengthens us and keeps us firm in the faith until we (**die**—sin).

2. Saul threatened to kill the (enemies—**followers**) of Jesus.

3. Saul was on his way to (reward—**capture**) Christians in Damascus.

4. After Jesus spoke to Saul on the road, Saul became a Christian (persecutor—**himself**).

5. Saul was baptized and became a (soldier—**missionary**) named Paul.

In Words of My Own

1. What was God's will for Paul? **God wanted Paul to become a Christian missionary**.

2. What is God's will for you and for all people? **God wants all people to be saved and to remain firm in His Word and faith.**

The Fourth Petition

(MFC 62)

Give us this day our daily bread.

Words to Use

Savior
live
work
blessings
friends

1. God gives us everything we need to **live**.

2. In the Fourth Petition we thank God for His many **blessings**.

3. We thank God for giving us meaningful **work** to do.

4. We thank God for giving us good **friends** with whom we can share our joys and sorrows.

5. Jesus is not only our **Savior**; He is our best and truest friend.

According to God's Word

1. In addition to food and clothes, God also gave Paul good (spouses—**friends**).

2. Paul's friends Priscilla and Aquila spent time with Paul making (**tents**—clothes).

3. As Paul and his friends worked together, they talked about (**Jesus**—camping).

In Words of My Own

1. What blessings has God given you to make your life comfortable and enjoyable? **Answers will vary somewhat. God has given us and all people everything we need to live and to enjoy living**.

2. Why is Jesus God's best gift to you? **God's best gift is the salvation His Son earned for us and for all people through His life, death, and resurrection**.

The Fourth Petition
(MFC 63)

What does this mean?

What is meant by daily bread?

Words to Use

everything

prayers

thanksgiving

men

daily

1. God gives **daily** bread to everyone.

2. In the Fourth Petition we ask God to help us to realize His goodness to us and to help us receive our blessings with **thanksgiving**.

3. God continues to bless us even without our **prayers**.

4. Daily bread includes **everything** that has to do with the support and needs of the body.

5. Jesus told His disciples, "From now on you will catch **men**."

According to God's Word

1. God gives daily bread also to those who are (dead—**evil**).

2. Jesus did a miracle before He (**called**—denounced) His first disciples.

3. The miracle involved their (**work**—hobby) of fishing.

4. When the disciples did as Jesus asked, they caught so many fish their (hearts—**nets**) began to break.

In Words of My Own

1. Why does God give good things to all people? **God is generous and loving.**

2. What did Jesus' words to His disciples mean? By "catching men" **Jesus meant that His disciples would share the Good News so that others would come to know and believe in Him.**

3. What did the disciples leave behind to follow Jesus? **The disciples left everything and followed Him.**

The Fifth Petition

(MFC 64)

And forgive us our trespasses
as we forgive those who trespass
against us.

Words to Use

perfume

tears

hair

guest

trespasses

1. In the Fifth Petition we pray that God will forgive our sins, or **trespasses**.

2. Jesus was once a **guest** in someone's house.

3. A woman washed Jesus' feet with her **tears**.

4. She dried Jesus' feet with her **hair**.

5. Then she poured **perfume** on Jesus' feet.

According to God's Word

1. The woman washed Jesus' feet at (**dinner**—breakfast).

2. The woman had lived a (holy—**sinful**) life.

3. The woman came up to Jesus and began to (**cry**—speak).

4. The woman (powdered—**kissed**) Jesus' feet.

5. Jesus (scolded—**forgave**) the woman.

6. Jesus told the woman, "Your (worship—**faith**) has saved you; go in peace."

In Words of My Own

1. Why did the woman treat Jesus as she did? **The woman had faith; she knew that Jesus had forgiven her sins.**

2. What do Jesus' actions tell us about Him? **Jesus' actions show that He loves people and is eager to forgive their sins and impart salvation to those who believe in Him.**

3. Why could the woman now be at peace? **The woman knew that Jesus had forgiven and saved her.**

The Fifth Petition

(MFC 65)

What does this mean?

Words to Use

worthy

sins

grace

limits

punishment

1. We pray in the Fifth Petition that our Father in heaven would not deny our prayer because of our **sins**.

2. We are not **worthy** of the things for which we pray.

3. We ask that God would give to us the things we ask for because of His **grace**.

4. Because we are sinners, we deserve only God's **punishment**.

5. God's forgiveness for us in Christ Jesus knows no **limits.**

According to God's Word

1. Peter once asked Jesus if he should forgive someone up to (**seven**—seventy-seven) times.

2. Jesus told Peter he should forgive someone (seven—**seventy-seven**) times.

3. Once Jesus forgave Peter for denying (**Him**—his prayer).

4. No sin is too (**great**—holy) for God to forgive.

In Words of My Own

1. What message did Jesus give when He told Peter to forgive up to seventy-seven times? **God wants His followers to be generous in their forgiving of others.**

2. For what reason do believers in Jesus forgive others? **God's people forgive others because God in Christ has forgiven them.**

3. Describe the kind of forgiveness Jesus gives you. **God's forgiveness in Christ knows no limits.**

The Sixth Petition

(MFC 66)

And lead us not into temptation.

Words to Use

swear

wept

servant

proclaim

waited

1. Peter was bold enough to **proclaim** that He would never disown Jesus.

2. Peter **waited** in the courtyard for news of Jesus' trial.

3. The girl who pointed out Peter as a follower of Jesus was a **servant**.

4. As Peter denied knowing Jesus, he began to curse and **swear**.

5. Realizing what he had done, Peter went outside and **wept**.

According to God's Word

1. On the (morning—**night**) of Jesus' arrest, Peter declared that he would never disown Jesus.

2. Later that (morning—**night**) Peter awaited news of Jesus' trial.

3. Peter denied knowing Jesus with an (**oath**—apology).

4. Peter remembered the (blessing—**warning**) Jesus had given him.

5. After denying Jesus the third time, Peter (**realized**—repeated) what he had done.

In Words of My Own

1. How do we know that Peter was sorry for denying Jesus? **Realizing what he had done, Peter left and wept bitterly.**

2. How do we know that Jesus was willing to forgive Peter? **Jesus taught that His forgiveness knows no limits.**

The Sixth Petition
(MFC 67)

What does this mean?

Words to Use

God

Uz

devil

Satan

Job

1. **God** tempts no one.
2. Together with the world and our sinful flesh, the **devil** attacks us regularly.
3. **Job** was a faithful follower of the true God.
4. Another name for the devil is **Satan**.
5. Job lived in **Uz**.

According to God's Word

1. Giving in to temptation leads to false belief, despair, and other great shame and (**vice**—victory).
2. We pray in the Sixth Petition that we will (overlook—**overcome**) temptation.
3. Satan brought Job (**torments**—toys).
4. Job was covered with (dust—**boils**) from head to foot.
5. Job (cursed—**trusted**) God.
6. (**God**—Satan) helped Job resist temptation.

In Words of My Own

1. When will all believers finally win victory and no longer be tempted? **When our Lord takes us to heaven, we will finally be free from sin and temptation.**
2. How did Job regard God as he endured his suffering? **Job trusted in God.**
3. What can we learn about God from the story of Job? **God helped Job resist temptation, and He will do the same for us.**

The Seventh Petition
(MFC 68)

But deliver us from evil.

Words to Use

give

eat

protect

deliver

beg

1. A woman came to Jesus to **beg** Him to heal her daughter.

2. "It is not right to **give** the children's food to the dogs," Jesus said.

3. The woman agreed with Jesus, but she replied that dogs do sometimes **eat** food that falls from the master's table.

4. God wants us to ask Him to **protect** us.

5. In the Seventh Petition, we ask God to **deliver** us from pain, harm, and dangers.

According to God's Word

1. Once a (Levite—**Canaanite**) woman came to Jesus.

2. The woman didn't (**give**—speak) up asking Jesus to help her.

3. Jesus (**granted**—rebuffed) the woman's request.

4. "Your faith is (weak—**great**)!" Jesus said.

5. God has all the (time—**power**) to help us in the way He knows is best.

In Words of My Own

1. What does Jesus teach us to ask of God in the words of the Seventh Petition? **Jesus teaches us to ask God to deliver us from evil.**

2. What can we learn from the woman about prayer? **We can learn to be faithful and steadfast in prayer.**

The Seventh Petition
(MFC 69)

What does this mean?

Words to Use

rescue

summary

sorrow

evil

hour

1. We offer the Seventh Petition, the last petition in the prayer, in **summary**.

2. In the Seventh Petition, we ask God to **rescue** us.

3. We ask for deliverance from every **evil**.

4. We ask God for a blessed end when our last **hour** comes.

5. Luther calls this world a valley of **sorrow**.

According to God's Word

1. (**Jesus**—Lazarus) once told a story of a rich man and a poor man.

2 When both men died, angels carried the (rich—**poor**) man to heaven.

3. The (**rich**—poor) man went to hell.

4. The (rich—**poor**) man had faith.

5. People are taken to heaven on account of their (**faith in Jesus**—many good works).

In Words of My Own

1. Why did the rich man go to hell while the poor man went to heaven? **The rich man had many things, but he did not have faith. The poor man went to heaven because he trusted Jesus for salvation.**

2. From what evil is everyone delivered who trusts in Jesus as his or her Savior? **Ultimately Jesus will take all who believe in Him "from this valley of sorrow to Himself in heaven."**

The Conclusion
(MFC 70)

For Thine is the kingdom and the power and the glory forever and ever.* Amen.

What does this mean?

Words to Use

glorify

heard

commanded

promised

pleasing

1. We can be certain that the petitions we pray are **pleasing** to God.

2. God has **commanded** us to pray.

3. We can be certain that our petitions are **heard** by God.

4. God **promised** to hear our prayers.

5. Angels in heaven **glorify** God.

According to God's Word

1. (**Amen**—Alleluia) means, "Yes, yes, it shall be so."

2. The Apostle John wrote by (**inspiration**—rejection) of the Holy Spirit.

3. John describes thousands of angels praising God for the (**salvation**—wealth) He brings to God's people.

4. Jesus is the victorious (**Lamb**—Angel) of God.

In Words of My Own

1. Describe God's heavenly kingdom. **Answers will vary. Heaven is an eternal dwelling where followers of Jesus will live in perfect peace and happiness in the presence of God.**

2. Why is Jesus worthy to receive power and wealth and wisdom and strength and honor and glory and praise? **Jesus is worthy because He has lived a sinless life and died an atoning death in our place in order to save us.**

3. What victory did Jesus win for us? **Jesus won our victory over sin.**

*These words were not in Luther's Small Catechism.

The Sacrament of Holy Baptism
(MFC 73)

Holy Baptism

Words to Use

faith

family

Spirit

gift

body

1. God gives Baptism as a **gift** to His people.

2. We receive God's blessings by **faith** through Baptism.

3. In Baptism each of us becomes a member of the **family** of God.

4. We are all baptized by one **Spirit**.

5. We are all baptized into one **body**.

According to God's Word

1. God's Word teaches us to baptize in the (place—**name**) of the Father and of the Son and of the Holy Spirit.

2. In Baptism, God works forgiveness of sins, new life, and (standards—**salvation**).

3. The body into which believers are baptized is (**united in**—divided by) Christ.

In Words of My Own

1. What gifts are received in Baptism? **Through Baptism God gives me forgiveness of sins, new life, and salvation.**

2. What does it mean to be a member of the family of God through faith in Christ Jesus? **To be a member of the family of God is to be united through Baptism with God and other believers through faith in Christ Jesus.**

Holy Baptism: First Section
(MFC 74)

What is Baptism?

Words to Use

Galilee
Jordan
heaven
dove
water

1. Baptism combines God's Word with **water**.

2. Jesus came from **Galilee** to be baptized by John.

3. Jesus came to the **Jordan** River to be baptized by John.

4. The Holy Spirit came down like a **dove**.

5. God the Father spoke from **heaven**.

According to God's Word

1. Baptism (is—**is not**) just plain water.

2. As soon as Jesus was baptized, He came out of (Galilee—**the water**).

3. (**Heaven**—The river) opened after Jesus was baptized.

3. The Holy Spirit (**landed**—frowned) upon Jesus.

4. "This is My (**Son**—dove), whom I love," said God the Father.

5. "With Him I am well (**pleased**—thanked)," said God the Father.

In Words of My Own

1. What makes simple water into Baptism? **The water must be combined with the Word of God to have a valid Baptism.**

2. Identify the Father, Son, and Holy Spirit at Jesus' Baptism. **The Spirit descended in the form of a dove, Jesus was coming out of the water, and God the Father spoke from heaven and called Jesus His Son.**

Holy Baptism: First Section

(MFC 75)

Which is that word of God?

Words to Use

earth

nations

disciples

resurrection

mountain

1. After His **resurrection** Jesus gathered His followers together.

2. Jesus' **disciples** worshiped Him in the region of Galilee.

3. Jesus spoke to His followers on a **mountain** in Galilee.

4. Jesus told them to make disciples of all **nations**.

5. Jesus told His followers to bring the Good News to everyone on **earth**.

According to God's Word

1. Jesus said, "All authority in heaven and on earth has been (**given to**—taken from) Me."

2. Jesus told His followers to baptize in the (place—**name**) of the Father and of the Son and of the Holy Spirit.

3. Jesus told His followers to teach people to (**obey**—ignore) everything He had commanded.

4. Jesus promised to (**be with**—send forth) His followers to the very end of the age.

5. These words of Jesus, also called the Great Commission, are recorded in the last chapter of (**Matthew**—Mark).

In Words of My Own

1. What words of God are Christians to use to baptize people? **Christians use the words "In the name of the Father, and of the Son, and of the Holy Spirit" in a baptism.**

2. What comforting assurance do God's people have as they share the Gospel? **As God's people, we have the assurance through faith that God is with us always, to the very end of the age.**

Holy Baptism: Second Section

(MFC 76)

What benefits does Baptism give?

Words to Use

belongs

rescues

gives

works

promises

1. Baptism **works** forgiveness of sins.

2. Baptism **rescues** from death and the devil.

3. Baptism **gives** eternal salvation to all who believe.

3. The words and **promises** of God tell us of the benefits of Baptism.

4. Referring to children, Jesus said, "The kingdom of God **belongs** to such as these."

According to God's Word

1. (**People**—The disciples) were bringing little children to Jesus.

2. (Jesus—**The disciples**) tried to keep the children away.

3. Jesus was not pleased with the (children—**disciples**).

4. "Let the (**children**—disciples) come to Me," Jesus said, "and do not hinder them."

In Words of My Own

1. How does Jesus feel towards children? **Jesus loves children. "Let the children come to Me," He said.**

2. What blessings has Jesus given you through Baptism? **Through Baptism God has given me the forgiveness of sins, rescued me from death and the devil, and given eternal salvation to me and all who believe.**

Holy Baptism: Second Section

(MFC 77)

Which are these words and promises of God?

Words to Use

traveled

saved

told

baptized

condemned

died

1. Whoever believes and is baptized will be **saved**.

2. Whoever does not believe will be **condemned**.

3. Philip met a man as he **traveled**.

4. Philip **told** the man about Jesus.

5. Philip explained that Jesus **died** for the sins of the world.

6. Philip **baptized** the man.

According to God's Word

1. The man was an official in (pursuit—**charge**) of the treasury of Candace.

2. Candace was the queen of (**Ethiopia**—Isaiah).

3. The man was reading about a (**lamb**—bull) that was killed.

4. Philip told the man about how Jesus is the (**Savior**—ruler) of the world.

5. The man (**rejoiced**—rested) after being baptized.

In Words of My Own

1. What did the man from Ethiopia ask after he came to believe in Jesus? **He asked to be baptized.**

2. Why did the man act as he did after being baptized? **The Ethiopian rejoiced knowing that He had received God's blessings through faith in the washing of Holy Baptism.**

3. What words and promises of God are associated with Baptism? **God promises that "whoever believes and is baptized will be saved" (Mark 16:16).**

Holy Baptism: Third Section
(MFC 78-79)

How can water do such great things?

Words to Use

grace

plain

faith

rebirth

heirs

1. Without God's Word water is **plain** water and no Baptism.

2. Water does great things in Baptism because it is connected with God's Word and **faith** that trusts God's Word.

3. With the Word of God present there is a Baptism, that is, a life-giving water rich in **grace**.

4. God saved us through the washing of **rebirth** and renewal by the Holy Spirit.

5. Having been justified by His grace, we become **heirs** who have the hope of eternal life.

According to God's Word

1. Nicodemus was a (**Pharisee**—Samaritan).

2. Nicodemus came to see Jesus one (morning—**night**).

3. Jesus told Nicodemus that no one can enter the kingdom of God without first being (baptized—**born**) again.

4. Jesus told Nicodemus that whoever believes in Him shall not (suffer—**perish**) but have eternal life.

In Words of My Own

1. How would you answer Nicodemus's question? **All people can be born again through Holy Baptism.**

2. What kind of washing does the Holy Spirit do in Baptism? **The Holy Spirit washes away our sins in a "washing of rebirth and renewal."**

3. Explain how someone is born again in Jesus. **Someone is born again when the Holy Spirit works faith in Jesus in his or her heart through God's Word and the Sacraments. Then he or she receives Christ's forgiveness, strength to live a new life, and eternal salvation in His name.**

Holy Baptism: Fourth Section
(MFC 80-81)

What does such baptizing with water indicate?

Where is this written?

Words to Use

arise

live

die

buried

1. By daily contrition and repentance our sinful nature should be drowned and **die**.

2. Baptism indicates that a new person should daily emerge and **arise**.

3. We are **buried** with Christ through Baptism into death.

4. By remembering our Baptism, we too may **live** a new life.

According to God's Word

1. The Old Adam is our (**sinful nature**—first parent).

2. In Baptism the new man should arise (**daily**—at the Last Day).

3. The new life God gives us to live in Him is a life of righteousness and (**purity**—privacy) forever.

4. Christ was raised from the dead through the glory of (**the Father**—Baptism).

In Words of My Own

1. What does Baptism mean for the daily life of a Christian? **When we remember our Baptism each day we can confess our sins, receive the forgiveness Jesus earned for us, and, assured that we are forgiven, serve God in lives of willing obedience.**

2. How does God preserve us in our Baptism? **The Holy Spirit preserves us through His righteousness and rescuing strength, imparted to us through Word and Sacrament—the means of grace.**

Confession
(MFC 83)

What is confession?

What sins should we confess?

Words to Use

Pharisee
pastor
forgiveness
absolution
tax collector

1. The two parts of confession include confessing our sins and receiving **absolution**.

2. Absolution is received from the **pastor** as from God Himself.

3. **Forgiveness** is another word for absolution.

4. Jesus once told a story about a **Pharisee** and a tax collector.

5. The sins of the **tax collector** were forgiven.

According to God's Word

1. Before God we should plead guilty of (no— **all**) sins.

2. We should (**confess to**—withhold from) the pastor those sins that we know and feel in our hearts.

3. Jesus told a story about two men who went to the (**temple**—synagogue) to pray.

4. The Pharisee (**thanked**—blamed) God that he was not like other men.

5. The tax collector prayed, "God have (**mercy on**—fear of) me, a sinner."

In Words of My Own

1. From whom does the forgiveness pronounced by the pastor really come? **The forgiveness (absolution) pronounced by the pastor is given as from God Himself.**

2. Why did one man in Jesus' story go home with his sins forgiven while the other man did not? **The forgiven man showed humble repentance for his sins; the other man prayed to boast to God of his own goodness.**

Confession
(MFC 84)

Which are these?

Words to Use

praise

Psalms

place

prophet

1. Martin Luther tells us to think about our **place** in life according to the Ten Commandments as we approach confession.

2. Nathan the **prophet** once talked to David about his sin.

3. David offered thanks and **praise** to God for His forgiveness.

4. Many of David's songs are included in the book of **Psalms**.

According to God's Word

1. Luther says to ask yourself: "Are you a father, mother, son, daughter, husband, wife, or (**worker**—traveler)?"

2. Luther says to ask yourself: "Have you been disobedient, unfaithful, or (unhappy—**lazy**)?"

3. Luther says to ask yourself: "Have you been hot-tempered, (**rude**—ruthless), or quarrelsome?"

4. Luther says to ask yourself: "Have you (**hurt**—helped) someone by your words or deeds?"

5. Luther says to ask yourself: "Have you (**stolen**—saved something), been negligent, wasted anything, or done any harm?"

In Words of My Own

1. How did David feel after receiving assurance that his sins had been taken away? **David felt relieved that the burden of his sin was removed; he thanked and praised God for loving and forgiving him.**

2. How did God take away David's sins and yours? **God took away all sins through the life, death, and resurrection of Jesus.**

A Short Form of Confession
(MFC 85)

Words to Use

confessor

servant

sinner

master

penitent

1. The person making the confession is referred to as the **penitent**.

2. The person hearing the confession is referred to as the **confessor**.

3. The person making the confession might say, "I, a poor **sinner**, plead guilty before God of all sins."

4. The person making the confession might say, "I, sad to say, serve my **master** unfaithfully, for in this and that I have not done what I was told to do."

5. Jacob once said to God, "I am unworthy of all the kindness and faithfulness You have shown Your **servant**."

According to God's Word

1. Jacob once reflected on God's grace and (**goodness**—justice).

2. Jacob once (boldly—**humbly**) praised God for His mercy and love.

3. Jacob praised God for His kindness and (**faithfulness**—unfaithfulness).

In Words of My Own

1. What have been the consequences of your sin? **Answers will vary. As expressed in the short form of confession, our sins often hurt and diminish the quality of life of others.**

2. What do you believe about all the sins you have asked God to forgive for Jesus' sake? **Trusting in God's promises, I believe that all my sins have been forgiven for Jesus' sake.**

A Short Form of Confession
(MFC 86-87)

Words to Use

set
curse
quarrel
overcharging
speak

1. I commit a sin when I **quarrel** with my friends.
2. Another example of a sin is to **curse** at a parent.
3. Parents sin when they **set** a bad example by indecent words and deeds.
4. I sin when I hurt or **speak** evil of a neighbor.
5. The storeowner sins by **overcharging**, selling inferior merchandise, or giving less than was paid for.

According to God's Word

1. The Bible teaches us that the forgiveness we receive from our confessor is really (**God's**—false) forgiveness.
2. The words of Jesus recorded in Holy Scripture (**command**—forbid) believers to forgive one another.

3. The confessor may also (**comfort**—burden) the penitent with additional passages from God's Word.

In Words of My Own

1. Why can the forgiven Christian "go in peace"? **When we receive Christ's forgiveness, we receive His complete freedom from sin and guilt. As a result, we can go about our lives in peace, trusting in His love and rejoicing in this freedom from sin and guilt.**
2. How do we know that God desires to forgive our sins? **We know God desires to forgive our sins because He sent His Son to pay the price of that forgiveness.**

The Office of the Keys
(MFC 88-89)

What is the Office of the Keys?

Where is this written?

What do you believe according to these words?

Words to Use

Evangelist
valid
Christ
authority
church

1. The Office of the Keys is a special **authority** given by Christ to forgive sin.

2. Christ has given the Office of the Keys to His **church** on earth.

3. St. John the **Evangelist** recorded that Jesus gave the Office of the Keys to His disciples.

4. When called ministers deal with people according to God's Word, their actions are **valid** and certain.

5. When called ministers deal with people according to God's Word, it is as if **Christ** dealt with them Himself.

According to God's Word

1. The Office of the Keys authorizes the church to (**forgive**—withhold forgiveness from) repentant sinners.

2. The Office of the Keys authorizes the church to (absolve—**exclude**) openly unrepentant sinners from the Christian congregation.

3. Jesus gave this Office of the Keys to His disciples on the day of His (Baptism—**resurrection**).

4. When Jesus appeared to them, the disciples were (angry—**overjoyed**).

5. Jesus said, "I am (forgiving—**sending**) you. Receive the Holy Spirit. If you forgive anyone his sins, they are forgiven; if you do not forgive them, they are not forgiven."

In Words of My Own

1. How should a Christian congregation and its members treat openly unrepentant members? **After loving and patient discussion with the person about their sin, the Christian congregation must exclude the unrepentant person from Holy Communion. The congregation must then work to bring the person to repentance and faith. The person becomes an object of their evangelism efforts.**

2. How would God have the members of His church regard those who repent of their sins? **Those who ask for and receive forgiveness for their sins are to be reinstated into the church and regarded once again as brothers and sisters in Christ.**

The Sacrament of the Altar

(MFC 90-91)

Words to Use

proclaim
drink
cup
broke
eat

1. We remember how Jesus gave His body for us when we **eat** the bread in the Sacrament of the Altar.

2. We remember how Jesus shed His blood for us when we **drink** the wine in the Lord's Supper.

3. When Jesus first gave the Sacrament, He **broke** the bread.

4. "This **cup** is the new covenant of My blood," Jesus said.

5. According to 1 Corinthians 11:23b-26, believers **proclaim** the Lord's death when they receive the Lord's Supper

According to God's Word

1. Jesus first gave the Lord's Supper on the (morning—**night**) of His betrayal.

2. Jesus took the bread and then gave (**thanks**—payment) for the bread.

3. Jesus said, "This is My (**body**—best).

4. Jesus took the (**cup**—candle) and began speaking about His blood.

5. Jesus said, "Do this, whenever you drink it, in (**remembrance**—fear) of Me."

Words of My Own

1. What two things do believers do, in remembrance of Jesus, in the Sacrament of the Altar? **In the Sacrament believers eat bread and drink wine.**

2. With regard to the Sacrament of the Altar, what are believers to do until Jesus comes? **Believers are to participate in the eating and drinking of the Sacrament to proclaim Jesus' death.**

The Sacrament of The Altar
(MFC 92-93)

What is the Sacrament of the Altar?

Where is this written?

Words to Use

poured

during

true

under

instituted

1. In the Sacrament of the Altar participants receive the **true** body and blood of our Lord Jesus Christ.

2. Participants in the Sacrament receive Christ's body and blood **under** the bread and wine.

3. The Sacrament has been **instituted** by Christ Himself.

4. Jesus gave His disciples the bread **during** the meal.

5. Jesus describes His blood as being **poured** out for many for the forgiveness of sins.

According to God's Word

1. The night before His (betrayal—**death**), Jesus gave His disciples the first Sacrament of the Altar.

2. Jesus shared the (**Passover**—Baptismal) meal with His disciples.

3. After Jesus took the cup, He gave (suggestions—**thanks**) and offered it to the disciples.

4. The holy Evangelists Matthew, Mark, and (**Luke**—John), as well as St. Paul, write about Jesus giving the Sacrament of the Altar.

5. Jesus (**shed**—shielded) His blood for the forgiveness of our sins.

In Words of My Own

1. To whom does Jesus refer when He says the words "for you"? **The words "for you" refer to those receiving the Sacrament.**

2. How do believers receive the Sacrament of the Altar? **Believers receive the Sacrament by eating the bread and drinking the wine.**

The Sacrament of the Altar

(MFC 94-95)

What is the benefit of this eating and drinking?

How can bodily eating and drinking do such great things?

Words to Use

drink

shed

given

forgiveness

eat

1. Christ's body was **given** for us for the forgiveness of our sins.

2. Christ's blood was **shed** for us for the forgiveness of our sins.

3. Participants in the Sacrament of the Altar receive Christ's body when they **eat** the bread.

4. Participants in the Sacrament of the Altar receive Christ's blood when they **drink** the wine.

5. Participants in the Sacrament of the Altar receive **forgiveness**.

According to God's Word

1. Where there is the forgiveness of sins, there is also (**life**—hope) and salvation.

2. God's words along with the (spiritual—**bodily**) eating and drinking are the chief things in the Sacrament.

3. Whoever believes Jesus' words has exactly what they say: "(fullness—**forgiveness**) of sins."

4. "For whenever you eat this bread and drink this cup, you (deny—**proclaim**) the Lord's death until He comes" (1 Corinthians 11:26).

In Words of My Own

1. In addition to eating and drinking, what is another essential part of the Sacrament of the Altar? **In addition to the bodily eating and drinking, the words "given and shed for you for the forgiveness of sins" are essential to the Sacrament.**

2. Along with forgiveness of sins, what else is received by those who participate in the Sacrament of the Altar? **In addition to the forgiveness of sins, life and salvation are given through the words "given and shed for you for the forgiveness of sins."**

The Sacrament of the Altar
(MFC 96)

Who receives this sacrament worthily?

Words to Use

require

fast

spread

cook

prepare

1. To **fast** and otherwise prepare to receive the Sacrament of the Altar is fine outward training.

2. The words "for you" **require** all hearts to believe.

3. While they lived in Egypt, God told His people to **prepare** a special lamb.

4. God's people were to **cook** and eat the lamb.

5. God's people **spread** the lamb's blood on the doorframe of their homes.

According to God's Word

1. Anyone who does not believe God's words is (unhappy—**unworthy**) to receive the Sacrament.

2. Anyone who does not believe God's words is (**unprepared**—unpredictable).

3. On (**Passover**—Easter) night the angel of the Lord killed the firstborn of every house that did not have blood on the doorframe.

4 (Jesus—**Pharaoh**) commanded God's people to leave Egypt.

5. God delivers His people from the (**slavery**—victory) of sin through the blood of Jesus.

In Words of My Own

1. Why should unbelievers not participate in the Sacrament of the Altar? **Anyone who does not believe in the forgiveness Jesus earned for all people is unworthy and unprepared to receive the Sacrament.**

2. How does the Sacrament of the Altar remind us of the Passover? **At the Passover God's people were saved by the blood of the lamb spread on their doorposts. In the Sacrament of the Altar God saves believers through the true body and blood of Jesus, the Lamb.**

Daily Prayers
(MFC 98-99)

Morning and Evening Prayer

Words to Use

keep

cross

forgive

name

place

1. Luther suggests that upon rising in the morning and upon going to bed at night believers make the sign of the **cross**.

2. When we pray in the **name** of the Father and of the Son and of the Holy Spirit, we remember our Baptism.

3. We ask that God will **keep** us safe from sin and all evil.

4. In our prayer we **place** ourselves into the hands of God.

5. In the evening prayer we ask God to **forgive** the sins we have committed.

According to God's Word

1. Luther suggests that at morning and at night Christians repeat the (**creed**—concordance) and the Lord's Prayer.

2. Both morning and evening prayers begin with an expression of (regret—**thanks**).

3. In both prayers we ask God to send His holy (apostles—**angel**) to be with us.

4. In both prayers we ask that the evil (**foe**—thought) will have no power over us.

In Words of My Own

1. Why can God's people be happy after placing themselves in the hands of God? **We rest safe and secure in God's Word and promises, confident in His love and care for us.**

2. Why do Christians pray in Jesus' name? **Christians pray in Jesus' name because only through Jesus' life, death, and resurrection can we become the children of God and have eternal life.**

Daily Prayers
(MFC 100)

Asking a Blessing

Returning Thanks

Words to Use

hope
love
food
bountiful
benefits

1. God gives **food** at the proper time to every living thing.

2. God's **love** endures forever.

3. God provides for us out of His **bountiful** goodness.

4. God delights in those who put their **hope** in His unfailing love.

5. God joyfully receives our thanks for all the **benefits** He provides.

According to God's Word

1. God opens His (**hand**—mind) and satisfies the desires of every living thing.

2. When Christians pray, Luther suggests that they pray reverently and that they (**fold**—wash) their hands.

3. God gives food to every (demon—**creature**).

4. Luther suggests that Christians pray the (**Lord's**—Sinner's) Prayer before and after eating.

5. The table prayers are directed to God the (**Father**—Spirit).

In Words of My Own

1. How does God regard those who put their hope in His unfailing love? "**God delights in those who fear Him, who put their hope in His unfailing love.**"

2. Why do Christians thank God for the food they eat? **Without our desiring or meriting it, God continues to feed and clothe us and otherwise provide for our needs. This is the reason for our thanks.**

Table of Duties
(MFC 102-103)

To Bishops, Pastors, and Preachers

What the Hearers Owe Their Pastors

Words to Use

respect

doctrine

obey

reproach

convert

1. The pastor (overseer) must be an honorable person, above **reproach**.

2. The pastor should manage his family well and see that his children **obey**.

3. The children of the pastor should show him **respect**.

4. The pastor should not be a recent **convert**.

5. The pastor should encourage others by teaching sound **doctrine**.

According to God's Word

1. Those who preach the gospel should make their (**living**—demands) by the gospel.

2. Anyone who receives (**instruction**—justice) in the word must share all good things with his instructor.

3. Those who preach and teach in the church are worthy of (**double**—half) honor.

4. God's people are to live at (**peace**—odds) with one another.

5. God wants His people to obey their leaders so that their work is a (**joy**—burden).

In Words of My Own

1. What makes the work of a pastor or other workers in the church so special? **Preaching and teaching the Word of God is a special honor.**

2. Summarize how God wants His people to regard those who serve them in His church. **God wants us to provide for those who instruct us in the Word. He commands us to obey those who watch over us so that their work will be a joy, not a burden.**

Table of Duties
(MFC 104-105)

Of Civil Government

Of Citizens

Words to Use

authorities

elders

rulers

agent

servant

1. Paul reminded the **elders** of the church at Ephesus of his ministry among them.

2. God's Word says that everyone must submit himself to the governing **authorities (rulers)**.

3. Those who do right have nothing to fear from **rulers (authorities)**.

4. The one in authority is God's **servant**.

5. A person in authority is an **agent** of wrath to bring punishment on the wrongdoers.

According to God's Word

1. Paul told those in Ephesus to turn to God in repentance and to have faith in (**Jesus**—themselves).

2. After they prayed together, the elders (**accompanied**—abandoned) Paul to the ship.

3. There is no authority except that which God has (**established**—forbidden).

4. Do what is right and the one in authority will (**commend**—apprehend) you.

5. Give to Caesar what is (God's—**Caesar's**).

In Words of My Own

1. What attitude does God want His children to have toward those in authority? **God would have us submit to governing authorities as we submit to God Himself.**

2. Explain what it means to "give to God what is God's." **God is the highest authority. God wants us to obey both the secular government and the higher Law that He Himself has established.**

Table of Duties
(MFC 106-107)

To Husbands, To Wives

To Parents, To Children

Words to Use

commend

peaceful

considerate

godliness

enjoy

1. God's Word tells us to pray for those in authority so that we may live **peaceful** and quiet lives.

2. God's Word tells us to pray for those in authority so that we may live in **godliness** and holiness.

3. Those in authority have the power both to punish and to **commend**.

4. Husbands are to be **considerate** as they live with their wives.

5. Children are to obey their parents to that it may go well with them and that they may **enjoy** long life on the earth.

According to God's Word

1. Timothy's mother, (Lois—**Eunice**), and his grandmother both loved Jesus.

2. Paul once reminded (Lois—**Timothy**), "From infancy you have known the holy Scriptures, which are able to make you wise for salvation through faith in Christ Jesus" (2 Timothy 3:15).

3. Husbands are to (worship—**love**) their wives as Christ loved His church.

4. Wives are to submit to their husbands as to (**the Lord**—their children).

5. To children God says to "(**honor**—reject) your father and your mother."

In Words of My Own

1. Why is God's Word so important? **God's Word is able to make us wise about the salvation we have through faith in Christ Jesus.**

2. Who told you about Jesus and His love for you? **Answers will vary but are likely to include parents and other family members, pastors, and teachers.**

Table of Duties

(MFC 108-109)

To Workers of All Kinds

To Employers and Supervisors

To Youth

To Widows

To Everyone

Words to Use

summed

treat

obey

humble

clothe

1. God wants us to **obey** our earthly masters.

2. Employers and supervisors are to **treat** those over whom they have authority with respect and fear and with sincerity of heart.

3. God opposes the proud but gives grace to the **humble**.

4. God's Word encourages us to **clothe** ourselves with humility toward one another.

5. The commandments are **summed** up in this one rule: "Love your neighbor as yourself."

According to God's Word

1. We are to obey those in authority, not only to win their (**favor**—obedience) when they are watching.

2. We are to serve wholeheartedly, as if serving the (**Lord**—employer).

3. There is no (**favoritism**—fraternizing) with God.

4 The young are to be submissive to those who are (**older**—sincere).

5. The widow who is left all alone puts her hope in God and (**prays**—sleeps).

In Words of My Own

1. Describe how God would have us treat those in authority over us? **God would have us serve those in authority wholeheartedly, as if serving the Lord.**

2. When we know the love of God in Christ Jesus, how will we relate to other people? **God's love compels us to love, serve, and pray for others.**

Christian Questions with Their Answers

(MFC 110-111)

Words to Use

wrath

Gospel

hope

commandments

shed

1. Because I have not kept the **commandments**, I know I am a sinner.

2. Because I am a sinner, I deserve only God's **wrath** and displeasure.

3. Because of Jesus, I **hope** to be saved.

4. Because Jesus died for me and **shed** His blood for me, I trust in Him.

5. Because I believe the holy **Gospel**, I know that Jesus died for me.

According to God's Word

1. I know I am a sinner because I have not (**kept**—seen) the Ten Commandments.

2. Christ is the (**Son**—Father) of God.

3. There is (**one**—three) God(s).

4. God the Father (did—**did not**) die for me.

5. The (Father—**Son**) is true God and also true man.

In Words of My Own

1. What do you deserve according to God's Word? **According to God's Word, because of their sin all people deserve only God's wrath and displeasure, temporal death, and eternal damnation.**

2. What has Christ done to bring you salvation? **He died for me and shed His blood for me on the cross.**

Christian Questions with Their Answers

(MFC 112-114)

Words to Use

drink

remember

eat

love

believe

1. Jesus took bread, gave thanks, broke it, and gave it to the disciples and said, "Take, **eat**; this is My body, which is given for you."

2. Jesus took the cup, gave thanks, gave it to the disciples, and calling the wine His blood said, "This do, as often as you **drink** it, in remembrance of Me."

3. Those partaking worthily in the Sacrament **believe** that the true body and blood of Christ are in the Sacrament.

4. When we eat and drink in the Sacrament we **remember** and proclaim Christ's death and the shedding of His blood.

5. Christ died to make full payment for sin because of His great **love** for His Father and for me and other sinners.

According to God's Word

1. Christians remember and proclaim Christ's death so we may learn to believe that no (**creature**—God) could make satisfaction for our sins; only Christ could do that.

2. We should encourage one another to receive the Sacrament (**frequently**—daily).

3. A person who does not feel the need for the Sacrament should (**believe**—refute) what Scriptures say about our bodies in Galatians 5 and Romans 7.

4. A person who does not feel the need for the Sacrament should look around to see whether he is still in the (war—**world**).

5. A person who does not feel the need for the Sacrament should also remember the continual lying and murdering influence of the (judge—**devil**).

In Words of My Own

1. Why is the Sacrament referred to as "no child's play"? **Matters relating to the Holy Sacrament are serious and not to be engaged in lightly. They relate to Christ's very body and blood in, with, and under the bread and wine being given for our salvation**.

2. Why do you wish to receive the Sacrament? **Answers will vary; best answers express a desire to receive the blessings of forgiveness and strength in Christ offered through the Sacrament.**

Books of the Bible

(MFC 116-117)

Words to Use

Prophetic

Pentateuch

Poetic

Historical

Epistles

1. The first five books of the Bible are referred to as the **Pentateuch**.

2. The first seventeen books of the Bible are **Historical** books.

3. Job and Proverbs are examples of **Poetic** books.

4. Revelation is a **Prophetic** book found in the New Testament.

5. Colossians is one of the **Epistles**.

According to God's Word

1. (**Ezekiel**—Job) is one of the Major Prophets.

2. (Daniel—**Joel**) is one of the Minor Prophets.

3. (Song of Songs—**Malachi**) is the last book in the Old Testament.

4. Three epistles included in the Bible were written by (Peter—**John**).

5. The one historical book found in the New Testament that is not named after the apostle who wrote it is (**Acts**—Jude).

In Words of My Own

1. Into what two parts is the Bible divided? **The Bible is divided into the Old and New Testaments.**

2. What is the main message of the Bible? **The main message of the Bible is that all people have sinned and that the free gift of salvation comes to all by God's grace through faith in Christ Jesus.**

Creeds and Confessions

(MFC 118-119)

Words to Use

Smalcald

Concord

Athanasian

Nicene

Augsburg

1. The **Nicene** Creed is often confessed at celebrations of the Lord's Supper.

2. The **Athanasian** Creed is read on Holy Trinity Sunday.

3. The **Augsburg** Confession was written by Philip Melanchthon.

4. The **Smalcald** Articles summarize Luther's main disagreements with the Roman Church.

5. The Formula of **Concord**, completed in 1577, served to resolve doctrinal differences among Lutherans.

Understanding the Confessions

1. Published in 1580, The Book of (**Concord**—Faith) is a true and unadulterated statement and exposition of the Word of God.

2. The (**Large**—Small) Catechism is not made up of questions and answers but presents basic Christian teachings in a form often used in sermons.

3. A well-known statement of faith written by Philip Melanchthon was read before Emperor (Maximilian—**Charles V**) in Augsburg, Germany, in 1530.

4. (**Melanchthon**—Luther) wrote a Treatise on the Power and Primacy of the Pope.

5. The Formula of Concord (**was**—was not) an exposition and defense of previously adopted writings.

In Words of My Own

1. What was Luther's purpose in writing the Small Catechism? **Together with the Large Catechism, the Small Catechism was intended by Dr. Luther to be a helpful manual for pastors and family heads to use to help teach God's Word to children and adults.**

2. What important doctrine makes up half of the Apology of the Augsburg Confession? **Half of the Apology is devoted to the Biblical doctrine of justification by grace through faith in Jesus Christ.**

The Church Year

(MFC 120-123)

Sundays and Major Festivals

Minor Festivals

Words to Use

Ash Wednesday

Nativity

Reformation

Transfiguration

Pentecost

1. Another name for Christmas is the **Nativity** of our Lord.

2. The **Transfiguration** of our Lord occurs at the end of the season of Epiphany.

3. **Ash Wednesday** marks the beginning of Lent.

4. The festival of **Pentecost** marks the end of the Easter Season.

5. **Reformation** Day is October 31.

Understanding the Church Year

1. The Ascension of our Lord is observed during the (Epiphany—**Easter**) season.

2. The first Sunday after Pentecost honors the Holy (Sacraments—**Trinity**).

3. The Circumcision of Our Lord is observed on (**New Year's**—St. Valentine's) Day.

4. On June 24 the Nativity of John (**the Baptist**—the Evangelist) is observed.

5. All Saints' Day is the first of (**November**—December).

In Words of My Own

1. Name the three major times of the church year. **The three major seasons of the church year are the Time of Christmas, the Time of Easter, and the Time of the Church.**

2. What difference do you find between the major and minor festivals of the church? **Major festivals focus on God's actions to rescue and save His people. Minor festivals include observances connected with saints and the history of the Christian church.**

I Am Jesus' Little Lamb

(MFC 124)

Words to Use

bids

guides

calls

provides

loves

1. Jesus the Good Shepherd gently **guides** me through my life.

2. Jesus **provides** for me by meeting my needs.

3. Jesus **loves** me every day with the same unending care.

4. Jesus **bids** me go to where the quiet waters flow.

5. Jesus **calls** me by my name.

According to God's Word

1. Knowing Jesus, I can be (**glad**—sad) at heart.

2. According to the hymn Jesus is my staff and (**stay**—way), meaning that He keeps me steady as I journey through life.

3. Jesus leads me into pleasant (**pastures**—palaces).

4. The third verse of the hymn describes each human life as (**short**—long).

5. In heaven we will rest in the (place—**arms**) of Jesus.

In Words of My Own

1. How is Jesus like a Good Shepherd? **Jesus gently guides us, knows our needs and provides for us, loves us, and calls us by name; finally He will take us to live with Him in heaven.**

2. What does Jesus mean to you as you live your life? As you look forward to eternity? **Jesus cares for us and guards, guides, and protects us as we live each day; at last He will take us to live with Him forever in the happiness and joy of heaven.**

God's Own Child, I Gladly Say It

(MFC 126-127)

Words to Use

release

unraveled

pay

sleep

comfort

1. Because I could not **pay** redemption's price, God made the payment Himself.

2. Through Baptism I have **release** from a guilty conscience.

3. Through Baptism the might of Satan is **unraveled**.

4. I have lifelong **comfort** knowing I am baptized into Christ.

5. Because I am baptized into Christ, I can **sleep** secure, even in my grave.

Understanding Hymns

1. In Baptism God (**unites**—contends) with me.

2. Because of Jesus I die to (**inherit**—promote) paradise.

3. Even in death the Christian's (**faith**—appearance) brightly flashes.

4. While my body rests in the ground, my soul will continue (amazing—**praising**) God.

5. Through faith in Jesus, I'm a child of (Mary—**paradise**).

In Words of My Own

1. Describe the blessings that are yours in Baptism. **Through Baptism God's people receive salvation, comfort, forgiveness and freedom from guilt, unity with God, unending gladness, and a home in paradise.**

2. Explain the term "forgiving flood" as used to explain Baptism. **In Baptism Jesus pours out His forgiveness freely and abundantly to all who receive it in faith.**

Lord, Help Us Ever to Retain

(MFC 128)

Words to Use

pray
absolve
faith
Sacrament
truth

1. In the Catechism, Luther taught God's Word of **truth**.

2. In this hymn we pray that we might turn from sin to God in **faith**.

3. We ask God to hear us when we **pray**.

4. We also pray that God would forgive or **absolve** us of our sin.

5. We conclude the hymn asking God to increase our faith through the **Sacrament**.

Understanding Hymns

1. Luther wrote the catechism in (sophisticated—**simple**) style.

2. Luther wrote the catechism to be taught to (patriarchs—**youth**).

3. Our God is referred to as The (One—**Three**) in One.

4. We (provide—**need**) God's help every day.

5. God brings children to Himself through (**Baptism**—condemnation).

In Words of My Own

1. Why did Martin Luther write the catechism? **Martin Luther wrote the catechism to help parents teach God's Word in a clear way.**

2. Summarize the Six Chief Parts of Christian doctrine as explained in this hymn. **God's Law (the Ten Commandments) shows us our sin and the need for the salvation offered only through the Triune God, described in the Apostles' Creed. The Lord's Prayer shows us how to communicate with God as children who have entered His family through Holy Baptism. Through Confession and Absolution we live each day in light of our Baptism and prepare to receive the Sacrament of the Altar through which the Spirit strengthens our faith.**

Soli Deo Gloria!

The Ten Commandments

The First Commandment

You shall have no other gods. (Exodus 20:3)

The Second Commandment

You shall not misuse the name of the LORD your God. (Exodus 20:7)

The Third Commandment

Remember the Sabbath day by keeping it holy. (Exodus 20:8)

Love your neighbor as yourself. (Matthew 22:39)

The Fourth Commandment

Honor your father and your mother. (Exodus 20:12)

The Fifth Commandment

You shall not murder. (Exodus 20:13)

The Sixth Commandment

You shall not commit adultery. (Exodus 20:14)

The Seventh Commandment

You shall not steal. (Exodus 20:15)

The Eighth Commandment

You shall not give false testimony against your neighbor. (Exodus 20:16)

The Ninth Commandment

You shall not covet your neighbor's house. (Exodus 20:17a)

The Tenth Commandment

You shall not covet your neighbor's wife, or his manservant or maidservant, his ox or donkey, or anything that belongs to your neighbor. (Exodus 20:17b)

The Close of the Commandments

What does God say about all these commandments? He says: "I, the LORD your God, am a jealous God, punishing the children for the sin of the fathers to the third and fourth generation of those who hate Me, but showing love to a thousand generations of those who love Me and keep My commandments." [Ex. 20:5-6]

The Apostles' Creed

I believe in God the Father Almighty, Maker of heaven and earth.

And in Jesus Christ, His only Son, our Lord, who was conceived by the Holy Spirit, born of the Virgin Mary, suffered under Pontius Pilate, was crucified, died and was buried. He descended into hell. The third day He rose again from the dead. He ascended into heaven and sits at the right hand of God, the Father Almighty. From thence He will come to judge the living and the dead.

I believe in the Holy Spirit, the holy Christian church, the communion of saints, the forgiveness of sins, the resurrection of the body, and the life everlasting. Amen.

The Lord's Prayer

Our Father who art in heaven, hallowed be Thy name, Thy kingdom come, Thy will be done on earth as it is in heaven. Give us this day our daily bread; and forgive us our trespasses as we forgive those who trespass against us; and lead us not into temptation, but deliver us from evil. For Thine is the kingdom and the power and the glory forever and ever. Amen.

Baptism

FIRST

What is Baptism?

Baptism is not just plain water, but it is the water included in God's command and combined with God's word.

Which is that word of God?

Christ our Lord says in the last chapter of Matthew: "Therefore go and make disciples of all nations, baptizing them in the name of the Father and of the Son and of the Holy Spirit." [Matt. 28:19]

SECOND

What benefits does Baptism give?

It works forgiveness of sins, rescues from death and the devil, and gives eternal salvation to all who believe this, as the words and promises of God declare.

Which are these words and promises of God?

Christ our Lord says in the last chapter of Mark: "Whoever believes and is baptized will be saved, but whoever does not believe will be condemned." [Mark 16:16]

THIRD

How can water do such great things?

Certainly not just water, but the word of God in and with the water does these things, along with the faith which trusts this word of God in the water. For without God's word the water is plain water and no Baptism. But with the word of God it is a Baptism, that is, a life-giving water, rich in grace, and a washing of the new birth in the Holy Spirit, as St. Paul says in Titus, chapter three:

"He saved us through the washing of rebirth and renewal by the Holy Spirit, whom He poured out on us generously through Jesus Christ our Savior, so that, having been justified by His grace, we might become heirs having the hope of eternal life. This is a trustworthy saying." [Titus 3:5-8]

FOURTH

What does such baptizing with water indicate?

It indicates that the Old Adam in us should by daily contrition and repentance be drowned and die with all sins and evil desires, and that a new man should daily emerge and arise to live before God in righteousness and purity forever.

Where is this written?

St. Paul writes in Romans chapter six: "We were therefore buried with Him through baptism into death in order that, just as Christ was raised from the dead through the glory of the Father, we too may live a new life." [Rom. 6:4]

Confession

What is confession?

Confession has two parts.

First, that we confess our sins, and

second, that we receive absolution, that is, forgiveness, from the pastor as from God Himself, not doubting, but firmly believing that by it our sins are forgiven before God in heaven.

What sins should we confess?

Before God we should plead guilty of all sins, even those we are not aware of, as we do in the Lord's Prayer; but before the pastor we should confess only those sins which we know and feel in our hearts.

Which are these?

Consider your place in life according to the Ten Commandments: Are you a father, mother, son, daughter, husband, wife, or worker? Have you been disobedient, unfaithful, or lazy? Have you been hot-tempered, rude, or quarrelsome? Have you hurt someone by your words or deeds? Have you stolen, been negligent, wasted anything, or done any harm?

The Office of the Keys

*What is the Office of the Keys?**

The Office of the Keys is that special authority which Christ has given to His church on earth to forgive the sins of repentant sinners, but to withhold forgiveness from the unrepentant as long as they do not repent.

*Where is this written?**

This is what St. John the Evangelist writes in chapter twenty: The Lord Jesus breathed on His disciples and said, "Receive the Holy Spirit. If you forgive anyone his sins, they are forgiven; if you do not forgive them, they are not forgiven." [John 20:22-23]

*What do you believe according to these words?**

I believe that when the called ministers of Christ deal with us by His divine command, in particular when they exclude openly unrepentant sinners from the Christian congregation and absolve those who repent of their sins and want to do better, this is just as valid and certain, even in heaven, as if Christ our dear Lord dealt with us Himself.

*This question may not have been composed by Luther himself but reflects his teaching and was included in editions of the catechism during his lifetime.

What is the Sacrament of the Altar?

It is the true body and blood of our Lord Jesus Christ under the bread and wine, instituted by Christ himself for us Christians to eat and to drink.

Where is this written?

The holy Evangelists Matthew, Mark, Luke, and St. Paul write:

Our Lord Jesus Christ, on the night when He was betrayed, took bread, and when He had given thanks, He broke it and gave it to the disciples and said: "Take, eat; this is My body, which is given for you. This do in remembrance of Me."

In the same way also He took the cup after supper, and when He had given thanks, He gave it to them, saying, "Drink of it, all of you; this cup is the new testament in My blood, which is shed for you for the forgiveness of sins. This do, as often as you drink it, in remembrance of Me."

What is the benefit of this eating and drinking?

These words, "Given and shed for you for the forgiveness of sins," show us that in the Sacrament forgiveness of sins, life, and salvation are given us through these words. For where there is forgiveness of sins, there is also life and salvation.

How can bodily eating and drinking do such great things?

Certainly not just eating and drinking do these things, but the words written here: "Given and shed for you for the forgiveness of sins." These words, along with the bodily eating and drinking, are the main thing in the Sacrament. Whoever believes these words has exactly what they say: "forgiveness of sins."

Who receives this sacrament worthily?

Fasting and bodily preparation are certainly fine outward training. But that person is truly worthy and well prepared who has faith in these words: "Given and shed for you for the forgiveness of sins." But anyone who does not believe these words or doubts them is unworthy and unprepared, for the words "for you" require all hearts to believe.

CPSIA information can be obtained at www.ICGtesting.com
Printed in the USA
LVOW09s2128140815

450186LV00009B/15/P